A UNIVERSITY GRAMMAR OF ENGLIS

workbook

A UNIVERSITY GRAMMAR OF ENGLISH

RANDOLPH QUIRK
SIDNEY GREENBAUM

workbook

R A Close

LONGMAN

LONGMAN GROUP LIMITED LONDON
Associated companies, branches and representatives throughout the world

First published 1974
ISBN 0 582 52280 3

Printed in Great Britain by
Lowe and Brydone (Printers) Ltd, Thetford, Norfolk

Preface

This Workbook is intended to assist students in their study of *A University Grammar of English* by Randolph Quirk and Sidney Greenbaum. It provides practice in applying the *Grammar's* principles and criteria and in dealing with many of the problems that the *Grammar* explains. The majority of the sentences, and all of the longer passages, that have been included as exercise material have been taken or adapted from authentic modern texts.

Anyone attempting to use the Workbook will immediately see that the exercises in it are not self-explanatory: they cannot be done properly—and in some cases cannot even be begun—until the relevant chapter or section of the *Grammar* has been carefully read. The exercises follow the order of the *Grammar* strictly.

Whether the exercises are done in the order in which they have been set, and exactly how they are done, are questions that are left to the judgment of the teacher conducting his own class, or to the student working on his own. The teacher may decide that a certain exercise is beyond the students he is teaching at the time. In that case the exercise can be done later. Sometimes an exercise can be profitably discussed in class before the students attempt to answer it on their own; and discussion on an exercise must involve reading and discussion of the relevant section of the *Grammar*.

When it comes to writing answers to the exercises, there are advantages in not doing this in the Workbook itself. Where tables are shown in the Workbook, this has only been done as an indication of how the student might present certain information in tabulated form.

Answers to exercises will be found in a key at the back of the Workbook. The objects of this key are (a) to give examples of the kind of answer expected, (b) to indicate what would be acceptable usage in cases where such information is not easily deducible from the *Grammar,* and (c) to provide, by symbols, a means of checking correct answers when this can be done objectively.

Answers have not been provided for every item in every exercise, for the reason that the author, having given examples of what sort of answer is required, has felt justified in hoping that students would be able to continue on their own. Their ability to do that depends, of course, on how well they will have studied the *Grammar*.

It should be emphasized that other answers than those given in the key may well be 'right', and that to organize possible answers according to 'degrees of correctness' would be pointless, as much depends on context, on particular shades of meaning, and on personal associations. But teachers and students may rest assured that the answers given in the key are acceptable and can be safely adopted.

I am most grateful to Professor Quirk and to Professor Greenbaum for their painstaking scrutiny of the exercises and the answers to them, and for numerous suggestions for improvement which I have gladly adopted.

R.A.C.

Acknowledgements
We are indebted to the following for permission to reproduce copyright material:
George Allen and Unwin Limited for an extract from *Portraits from Memory* by Bertrand Russell which has been slightly adapted.

1 Varieties of English

The objects of Exercises 1, 2 and 3 are to help the student to concentrate on the statements made in Chapter One; to familiarize him with technical terms used in it; and to give him an opportunity of applying its principles to actual examples of various kinds of English.

Exercise 1

Select one item from the left-hand column to replace each dash in the sentence on the right, so as to produce *a statement equivalent in meaning to one made or implied in the first chapter*.

1 British, American, Scottish, Canadian, regional, older, provincial	Technically, $_a$______ English is a dialect in so far as it is a $_b$______ variety of the language.
2 superior, inferior, equally related, equivalent, equal	One particular regional variety is $_a$______ to the others in every respect, and none need be regarded as $_b$______.
3 grammar, lexicon, phonology, vocabulary	The difference between one regional variety and another is most noticeable in $_a$______, and least of all in $_b$______.
4 dialectal, educated, uneducated, standard, officially recognized	The same features of $_a$______ English may be found in more than one of its $_b$______ forms.
5 educated speech, a dialect, adopted, used, regularized	Standard English is $_a$______ that has been $_b$______ by a number of academic and official bodies.

6 a, and, no, but, divergence, uniformity, grammar, spelling, pronunciation, standardization, vocabulary, idiom	There is a______ single standard form of English, b______ we find very considerable c______ in matters of d______, and even a remarkable lack of e______ in f______ and g______.
7 more, less, register, medium, style, possesses, lacks, employs, and, but	Written English is a a______ effective b______ of communication than spoken, in that it c______ certain prosodic features; d______ for that reason it has to be e______ precise.
8 social relationship, approach, attitude, what, why, whether	Whether a speaker decides to use formal or informal English depends partly on his a______ to his audience, partly on b______ he is communicating.
9 a corrupt form, interference, a new dialect, a new grammar, another variety	When foreign linguistic patterns leave a lasting influence on a language in a certain area, and a______ becomes permanent, then b______ of that language results.
10 generally, only, exclusively, adopted, recognized, public, private, government, educational, schools, colleges	Received Pronunciation is the name given to a type of speech a______ b______ by certain c______ d______ institutions, called e______ f______.
11 regional, standard, educated, style, register, medium, formal, neutral, informal	One would expect an American biologist, wishing to publish an article on his special subject, to use a a______ variety of English and a scientific b______, to adopt the written c______ and a d______ attitude to his readers.

12 *If I had known, Had I known, We have gotten, autumn,* formal, informal, British, American

$_a$________ is typical of $_b$________ English, while $_c$________ is characteristic of $_d$________, English.

Exercise 2

Say what features of the following passages are characteristic of *a* British or American English, *b* a particular register, *c* the spoken or the written medium, *d* formal or informal attitude, *e* substandard English.

Note

The purpose of this exercise is to accustom the student to use the terms *register* etc. in the way in which they have been used in Chapter One of the *Grammar*. Teachers will no doubt wish to discuss the exercise in class before it is attempted by the students. Ideas on the subject of it will be found not only in Chapter One of the *Grammar* but also in Crystal and Davy, *Investigating English Style* see the Bibliography in the *Grammar*.

1 I have recently been in correspondence with Messrs X and Y, Architects, concerning a number of irregularities which existed in the water supply installation at your Centre.

2 These bookshelves have become so popular that we've now added an extra unit. Also a writing-desk extension which you can fit to it. Why not give it a try?

3 We don't know nothing about it, sir, honest, we was never playing on the railway line, was we Dick?

4 Shut off supply to tap. Open tap fully to make sure water is shut off properly and leave open.

5 I appoint X Limited (hereinafter called 'The Company') to be the Executor and Trustee of this my Will on the Company's Terms and Conditions in force at the time of my death (including those governing the rights of the Company to remuneration and the incidence of such remuneration as set forth therein) –

6 What I wanted to ask you really was, as – m – I didn't know whether you were going to say that you could come or not, but I was going to suggest could you make it on the following Saturday?

7 As a biologist, I feel pretty sure that not all the knowledge an animal possesses has been founded upon experience it has enjoyed in its own lifetime.

8 On July 7, 1964, 3·9 millicuries of Cl-labeled DDT on inert granules were applied by helicopter to an enclosed four-acre marsh area at the rate of 0·2 pounds DDT per acre.

9 Pour coffee and syrup over crumbs. Sift dry ingredients and add. Stir in raisins.

10 In our time, we read too many new books, or are oppressed by the thought of the new books which we are neglecting to read; we read many books, because we cannot know enough people; we cannot know everybody whom it would be to our benefit to know.

11 Did you ever eat chicken?
Sure. I guess I've eaten chicken six or seven times.
What are you going to do when you grow up?
Shucks. I don't know.

12 A DRQ on a test flight from X to Y was reported missing last night and believed to have crashed in the Z highlands. Rescue teams planned to set out at first light today. There were two test pilots and two other crew on board.

Exercise 3
Quote, from each of the twelve extracts in Exercise 2, three or four grammatical constructions which you would consider as belonging unmistakably to a *common core* of English.

2 Elements of grammar

In doing Exercises 4–16, the student may be performing operations with which he is already familiar; and in subsequent chapters, he will find a more detailed treatment of some of the subjects dealt with here. The overlap is deliberate, the main object of Exercises 4–16 being to give the student confidence, before he proceeds with a study of the rest of the *Grammar,* in using the sort of criteria introduced in Chapter Two.

Operators

Exercise 4

Identify the whole of the subject of each of the sentences below. Then transform each sentence so as to form a *yes-no* question on the model:

Operator + subject + rest of the predicate,

and answer the question on one of the following models:

Yes + subject (pronoun) + operator;

No + ,, ,, + ,, + *n't*:

1 Computers are fairly commonplace today.
2 We have a computer here. (*Give two different transforms*)
3 Full-scale computers use a large number of programs.
4 These programs have to be changed from time to time.
5 A special period will need to be set aside for this operation.
6 Thinking about this led us to an interesting conclusion.
7 Someone having a dream could be performing a similar operation.
8 Most people have had the experience of dreaming in a feverish state.
9 Then the sleeper sees dreams as a jumbled sequence of unimportant detail.
10 This jumbled sequence of detail keeps dancing in front of his eyes.
11 The speaker is seriously comparing dreams with what happens in a computer.
12 The process of changing a computer programme can be compared with human dreams.

Constituent parts of a sentence

Exercise 5

Divide each of the sentences below into its *constituent parts,* and label each part *S, V, C, O* or *A,* as in models a and b:

S V C A
a Computers/are/fairly commonplace/today.
V– S A –V O
b /Did/you/ever/eat/chicken?

1 Full-scale computers have a large number of programs.
2 We must change all the programs tomorrow.
3 Tomorrow will be a holiday here.
4 These bookshelves are becoming very popular in Sweden.
5 We have recently added an extra unit to them.
6 Will you give it a try?
7 On July 7, DDT was sprayed on the marsh from a helicopter.
8 We all read too many books too quickly.
9 The young man grew restless in his mother-in-law's house.
10 They had made him their son-in-law despite his objections.
11 He found his mother-in-law greedy.
12 They had found him a charming young wife.

Subordinate or dependent clauses
Exercise 6
Pick out *the subordinate or dependent clause* in each of the sentences below. Label the constituent parts, both of the main clause and of the subordinate clause, and indicate the relationship between the two clauses, thus:
S V O S V O A
/You/must add/the raisins/after [you/'ve poured/the syrup/over the crumbs]
(A)

1 I don't believe that those bookshelves are popular anywhere yet.
2 What that advertisement says is not true.
3 What that advertisement says, I simply don't believe.
4 I'll believe it when I see the results.
5 Can you tell us when we shall see the results?
6 I was saying could you come next Saturday?
7 I guess I've eaten chicken six or seven times.
8 You didn't leave the tap open after you shut off the water supply.
9 Where the plane crashed, the snow is still falling heavily.
10 Where the plane crashed is still not known.

Objects and complements
Exercise 7
Indicate, by Od, Oi, Cs or Co whether the parts underlined in the sentences below are the *direct object* (Od), the *indirect object* (Oi), the *subject complement* (Cs) or the *object complement* (Co):

1 Will someone get a doctor, quickly!
2 George and Paul both became famous doctors.
3 Do you call [a]yourself a [b]doctor?
4 May I call [a]you [b]Jenny?
5 May I call [a]you [b]a taxi or something?
6 Call me anything you like.
7 It's [a]so cold. I can't get [b]warm.
8 I can't get [a]my hands [b]warm.
9 Keep [a]quiet. Keep [b]those children [c]quiet.
10 Can't you give [a]them [b]something to keep [c]them quiet?
11 The young man was slowly going mad.
12 His mother-in-law was driving [a]him [b]mad.
13 The driver turned the corner too quickly.
14 The weather is turning warmer.
15 The hot weather turned [a]all the milk [b]sour.
16 The young man grew very depressed.
17 He grew [a]his hair [b]long.
18 He had made a great mistake.
19 His in-laws had simply made [a]him [b]their servant.
20 His wife sometimes made [a]him [b]curry.
21 But this only made [a]him [b]more miserable.
22 Show [a]me [b]your passport. Show [c]me.
23 Did you see [a]anyone? Did you say [b]anything?
24 I didn't tell [a]anybody [b]anything.

Categories of verbs

Exercise 8

The following terms can be used with reference to verbs:

a intensive
b extensive
c stative
d dynamic
e intransitive
f monotransitive
g ditransitive
h complex transitive

Indicate, by the letters *a*, *b*, *c*, etc., which of those terms could be applied to the verbs as they are used in the sentences below. Note that more than one label could be used in every case.

1 Do you understand the question?
2 English and German are separate languages.
3 He appeared rather worried.
4 The mist is disappearing slowly.
5 I see[1] what you mean[2].
6 You aren't looking in the right direction.
7 He offered her his hand hesitatingly.

8 Bertrand is becoming rather a bore.
9 Susan chooses her clothes sensibly.
10 Her mother made her that dress well.
11 We elected him President unanimously.
12 His election made him very conceited.

Sentence structure

Exercise 9

Use one of the eight terms in the instructions to Exercise 8 to fill each gap in the sentences below most appropriately:

1 In a sentence with the structure S + V + *x*, if *x* is a noun that must be plural when S is plural, then V is
2 In the structure S + V + *x*, if both S and *x* are plural nouns, V may be either a——— or b———.
3 In the same structure, if S is plural and *x* is a singular noun, then V is usually—.
4 In S+V+A, if A can be realized by steadily, then V is a———, not b———.
5 If Od is present in a clause, V is either a——— or b——— or c———.
6 If Oi is present, V is ———.
7 If Co is present, V is ———.
8 In S+V+A, if A is realized by at this moment, V is not ———.
9 In any structure, if V is transitive it must be ———.
10 The progressive may occur if V is a——— but not if V is b———.

Exercise 10

Read the following passages:

a The Great Fire of London occurred in 1666. It started in a bakery in Pudding Lane, near London Bridge. It burnt furiously, and in four days it destroyed four-fifths of the city. It left about 100,000 people homeless. Samuel Pepys, the diarist, saw the fire from his home and has given us a vivid account of it.

b London's Big Ben, by the River Thames, has become famous throughout the world. It is not a clock, as many people think, but a huge bell inside the clock-tower. The Government awarded the contract for making it to Frederick Dent. In 1858, the bell was finished, and members suddenly decided to christen it Big Ben after Sir Benjamin Hall, one of their colleagues who was growing very stout and who had just made a long and witty speech.

Then, only using information contained in those two passages, form two sentences on each of the following *structural patterns*:

1 S+V stat. int. + Cs + A time.
2 S+V stat. int. + A place + A place.

3 S+V stat. trans.+Od+A place.
4 S+V dyn. int.+Cs+A place *or* time.
5 S+V dyn. monotrans.+Od+A time.
6 S+V dyn. ditrans.+Oi+Od.
7 S+V dyn. complex trans.+Od+Co.
8 A time+V dyn. ext. intrans.+A process.

Linguistic structures

Exercise 11

A part of each of the sentences below is underlined. Indicate by which of the following *linguistic structures* the underlined part is being realized:

a simple (=one-word) finite verb phrase
b complex finite verb phrase
c simple non-finite verb phrase (including infinitive with *to*)
d complex non-finite verb phrase
e finite clause
f non-finite clause
g prepositional phrase
h noun phrase
i adjective phrase
j adverb phrase

1 Fire can cause great damage to any city.
2 The Great Fire of London started in a bakery.
3 It burnt furiously for four days.
4 Pepys has given us a vivid account of it.
5 Who has given a vivid account of it?
6 The man who has just spoken is Benjamin Hall.
7 They suddenly decided to christen the bell Big Ben.
8 The idea occurred to them while Hall was speaking.
9 The man who won the contract was Dent.
10 The next day we were sitting in the car.
11 Leaving us at the gate, they disappeared.
12 Leaving us at the gate like that was very thoughtless.
13 Hand the man at the gate your ticket.
14 I never imagined that such a thing could happen.
15 The strange thing is that we never heard of him again.
16 I thoroughly enjoyed meeting June again.
17 Meeting her again has left me very happy.
18 There were the cakes, burnt to a cinder.
19 GRAVE DOUBTS WHETHER PEACE WILL LAST
20 Graves doubts whether agreement can be reached.

Parts of speech

Exercise 12

Classify the underlined words as parts of speech. If a word is underlined more than once, eg right, refer to the first occurrence as right (1), the second as right (2), and so on.

1 Is it right to say that right wrongs no man?
2 One cannot right all the wrongs in the world.
3 Cure that cold with a drink of hot lemon before you go to bed.
4 Drink this quick! Don't let it get cold.
5 Before the Fire, there had been a plague, the like of which had not been known before and has not been seen since.
6 It is a common failing to suppose we are not like other men, that we are not as other people are.
7 As your doctor, I must warn you that the results of taking this drug may be very serious.
8 Growth in weight results in the development of muscles and fat.
9 Warm pan, sift dry ingredients and stir well.
10 Dry hair thoroughly with warm towel and comb.

Stative and dynamic

Exercise 13

Indicate whether the underlined verb phrases are *stative* or *dynamic* in the context given:

1 This tank holds precisely 10 litres.
2 Hold the handle very firmly.
3 Answer the question more precisely.
4 He['s][a] a fool. [b]Don't listen to him.
5 I [a]was a fool. I [b]was driving too fast.
6 I'd like three tickets immediately.
7 We [a]have only two tickets, I['m][b] afraid.
8 I was having my coffee quietly.
9 [a]Smell this meat. [b]Does it smell bad?
10 I [a]think I [b]hear someone [c]coming.
11 I [a]consider you [b]acted very wisely.
12 We shall consider your application.

Pro-forms

Exercise 14

Replace each underlined part by a *pro-form* (which may consist of more than one word) which can be used when the information contained in the sentence is repeated:

1 The man who has just spoken is Benjamin Hall.
2 I never imagined that such a thing could happen.
3 An idea suddenly occurred to the Members present.
4 It occurred to them while Benjamin Hall was speaking.
5 Hand the man at the gate your ticket.
6 I said, 'The man at the gate!'
7 I'm afraid I haven't a ticket.
8 They'll be issuing some new tickets tomorrow.
9 They'll be issuing some new tickets tomorrow.
10 Ferguson saw the fire and Parkinson saw it too.
11 Are you sure the baker started it?
12 A Are we on the right road?
B Yes I think we're on the right road.
13 Well, I think we're not on the right road.
14 Do you enjoy walking in the rain?
15 Do you really want to get soaked through?
16 I would hate you to think that of me.
17 I believe he wants to be left alone.
18 You think you can't answer this question, but you can answer it.
19 If you haven't renewed your licence, you should renew your licence without delay.
20 If you haven't renewed it, you should renew it.

Wh-questions

Exercise 15

Form *Wh*-questions which will precisely elicit, as answers, the underlined parts of the following questions.

1 DDT was sprayed over the area.
2 Samuel Pepys wrote an account of the fire.
3 He wrote an account of the fire.
4 He wrote an account of the fire.
5 The fire started in a bakery.
6 It burnt furiously.
7 It burnt for four days.
8 That happened in 1666.
9 Pepys' account of it is the best.
10 Fires broke out every night during the war.
11 Twenty people were killed on the roads yesterday.
12 Three inches of rain fell last night.
13 It is four miles from here to the station.
14 It will only take you ten minutes to get there by car.
15 This castle was built during the fifteenth century.
16 The Aswan Dam was built to provide a reservoir for the Nile valley.

Assertion, non-assertion

Exercise 16

Provide one of the following labels for each of the sentences below:

assertion, positive and declarative
non-assertion, interrogative, positive
non-assertion, interrogative, negative
non-assertion, negative

Support your choice of label by evidence such as *some* or *any*.

1 Have you finished this chapter yet?
2 None of us have finished it yet.
3 Some of the others have finished it already.
4 Then why haven't you finished it yet?
5 Have you got much to do?
6 I never have much to do in the evening.
7 But I have quite a lot to do in the morning.
8 I haven't much to do in the morning, either.
9 I have plenty to do in the morning, too.
10 Haven't you got anything to do, either?

3 The verb phrase

The object of Exercises 17–19 is to help the student to make accurate statements about the English verb, using linguistic criteria and terminology. Exercises 20–44 provide practice in applying the rules and information given in Chapter Three.

Statements about the verb phrase

Exercise 17

Select one item from the left-hand column to replace each dash in the sentences below, so as to produce *statements EITHER equivalent in meaning to what is said in Chapter Three OR deducible from it.*

A
a
an
auxiliary
form
function
inflection
item
lexical
member
modal
noun
primary
syntactic
system
verb

1 A simple verb phrase that is not a pro-form can consist only of a______ b______ verb. One that is a pro-form can only consist of c______ d______.

2 The verb phrase *must be seen* contains three a______s. The last has the b______ of a c______ verb; the second has the d______ of a e______ f______; the first, the g______ of a h______ i______.

3 Whereas a______ verbs are open-class b______s, the c______ verbs are d______s of a closed e______.

4 We know that *work,* in the sentence *We work too hard,* is a a______, because of its b______ behaviour; and that the same word in a sentence beginning *I have work* . . . is a c______ because it has no d______.

5 The lexical verbs WILL and CAN have the same a______, in the base, as the b______ c______ verbs WILL and CAN, but their d______ is different.

B
base
consonant
defective
-ed
imperative

6 Regular verbs are a______ verbs whose b______ c______ and d______ e______ one can always f______ from the g______.

7 Modal auxiliaries are a______ verbs in that they have no b______, c______, d______, e______, f______ or g______.

infinitive inflection *-ing* lexical participle past phonological predict present tense voiceless voiced vowel	8 An irregular verb is one whose a______ b______ and c______ d______ one cannot e______ from the f______. 9 BURN has two a______ forms for V-*ed*, the difference between them being that the final b______ in one, spelt *-ed*, is c______, while in the other it is d______. 10 In BURN, there is no difference between V and V-*ed* in the a______ b______, whereas in DREAM the c______ d______ changes. In V-*ed*, both verbs have an e______ which may be f______ or g______.
C an auxiliary concord first imperative indicative lexical marked modal mood number operator overt subjunctive tense unmarked verb	11 A finite verb must be marked for a______, and may have b______ c______ with its subject in person and d______. 12 In the sentence *I suggest he go,* the second verb is a______ for b______ c______, while the first is in the d______, e______ f______. 13 In the sentence *You do the cooking,* <u>do</u> is a a______ verb and may be either in the b______ c______ or in the d______. 14 In the interrogative transformation, the a______ b______ is used as c______ d______ and changes places with the subject of the sentence. 15 In any complex verb phrase, the a______ b______ will come at the end, and the c______, if any, will come at the beginning.
D American aspect auxiliary clause English formulaic infinitive mandative non-finite passive perfective person	16 The *-ed* participle in a complex verb phrase may be a partial realization of either a______ b______ or c______ d______, the other part being provided by an e______ f______. 17 The *-ing* participle in a complex verb phrase is, combined with the a______ BE, a realization of b______ c______. 18 Either the *-ed* or the *-ing* participle, like the a______, may also be used alone, as a b______ c______ in a d______ e______. 19 Non-finite verbs are not marked either for a______ or b______, but may have c______ or d______ e______.

progressive
subjunctive
tense
verb
voice

20 The verb in *Heaven help us!* is an example of the a______ b______, whereas the c______ d______ in *I suggest he go* is still in active use, at least in e______ f______.

Exercise 18

Give accurate statements of the rules for:

a the phonological realization of V-*s*;
b the spelling of V-*s*;
c the phonological realization of V-*ed* in regular verbs;
d the spelling of V-*ed* in regular verbs;
e the doubling of final consonants in V-*ing* and V-*ed*.

Verb forms

Exercise 19

In what respect do the following forms conform to or deviate from the rules you have given in answer to Exercise 18?

a is
b has
c does
d goes
e says
f passes
g tries
h plays
i angling
j tinkling
k dying
l dyeing
m singing
n singeing
o agreeing
p picnicked
q developed
r occurred
s labelled
t travelled

Exercise 20

Complete the tables below, underlining any inflection which is pronounced as a separate syllable. Note: it is not suggested that answers should be written in the Workbook.

V	copy	dance	echo	exist	fix	gas	gallop	hate
V-*s*								
V-*ing*								
V-*ed*								

V	lay	lie	may	obey	offer	stretch	trap	visit
V-*s*								
V-*ing*								
V-*ed*								

Exercise 21
Identify each verb phrase in the sentences below. Call the first number one, and so on. Then indicate whether each verb phrase is finite or non-finite. If finite, say whether it is in present or past tense, in the indicative, imperative or subjunctive mood. If it has overt concord, quote its subject. If non-finite, say whether it is the infinitive, *-ing* participle or *-ed* participle.

A Die, doctor? That is the last thing I intend to do.
B Die, traitor! Every man found guilty of treachery pays the penalty.
C We found him lying by the roadside and were almost sure at first that he was dead.
D Having considered his case very carefully, we recommend that he serve another month on probation and be asked to appear before the committee when that has been done.
E Somebody bring me a map and show me where we are.
F I do understand. Please do believe what I'm trying to tell you.

Irregular verbs
Exercise 22
Consider the two V-*ed* forms of the 30 irregular verbs below:

beat	come	find	learn	sell	slide
begin	dig	fight	let	send	spell
build	drive	go	make	shine	spread
buy	fall	hold	meet	show	stand
break	feel	hurt	put	sit	stride

Then (a) re-arrange the 30 verbs in four groups as follows:
1 V, V-ed_1, V-ed_2 all alike — 2 V-ed_1 = V-ed_2, but not V
3 V = V-ed_2 but not V-ed_1 — 4 V, V-ed_1, V-ed_2 all different

Next, (b) choose one verb from the 30 for each of the following subdivisions of Groups 2 and 4.

Group 2, with /d/ or /t/ as suffix in V-ed
i Can also be regular
ii No change in base vowel, but final /d/ in V becomes /t/ in V-*ed*
iii No change in base vowel, but final consonant changes to /d/ in V-*ed*
iv Base vowel changes in V-*ed* to /e/, as in *bed*,
v ,, ,, ,, ,, V-*ed* ,, /ɔ/, ,, ,, *saw*
vi ,, ,, ,, ,, V-*ed* ,, /əʊ/, ,, ,, *home*

Group 2, without /d/ or /t/ as suffix in V-ed
vii Base vowel changes to /e/, as in *bed*
viii ,, ,, ,, ,, /ʌ/, ,, ,, *sun*
ix ,, ,, ,, ,, /ɑʊ/, ,, ,, *now*
x ,, ,, ,, ,, /i/ ,, ,, *sit* .

xi ,, ,, ,, ,, /æ/, ,, ,, *sat*
xii ,, ,, ,, ,, /ɐ/, ,, ,, *not*
xiii ,, ,, ,, ,, /ɔ/, ,, ,, *saw*
xiv ,, ,, ,, ,, /ʊ/, ,, ,, *put*
xv ,, ,, ,, ,, /əʊ/, ,, ,, *home*

Group 4
xvi Can also be regular
xvii V-ed_1 and V-ed_2 have the same vowel
xviii V and V-ed_2 ,, ,, ,, ,,
xix V, V-ed_1 and V-ed_2 all have different vowels
xx ,, ,, ,, ,, ,, ,, the same vowel

Exercise 23

Rapid drill in the use of irregular verbs. Make up dialogues, on the following model, replacing the phrase underlined in the model by each of the phrases below:

Model:
Have you ever *swallowed a plum stone?*
Yes, I have swallowed one.
When did you *swallow a plum stone?*
I swallowed one last year.

1 blow a bugle
2 break a toe-nail
3 build a shed
4 burst a tyre
5 buy a tape-recorder
6 catch a fish
7 choose a ring
8 cut a wisdom tooth
9 dig a deep hole
10 do a somersault
11 draw a map
12 drink a pint of cider
13 drive a truck
14 eat a bad shrimp
15 feed a tiger
16 fight a duel
17 find a wallet
18 fly a plane
19 get a bull's-eye
20 grind an axe
21 grow a lettuce
22 have an accident
23 hear a nightingale
24 hit a bus
25 hold a snake
26 keep a rabbit
27 lay a carpet
28 lead an expedition
29 learn a long poem
30 light a bonfire
31 lose a five-pound note
32 make an omelette
33 meet a film-star
34 read a Russian novel
35 ride a camel
36 ring an alarm bell
37 see a shark
38 sell a ticket
39 send a telegram
40 shine a beacon
41 sing a Chinese song
42 sink a boat
43 sow a melon seed
44 spill a bottle of ink
45 split a pair of trousers
46 steal a library book
47 strike a rock
48 swear an oath
49 sweep a floor
50 swing a lasso
51 take a sleeping pill
52 teach a lesson
53 tear a muscle
54 tell a fortune
55 throw a discus
56 tread on a scorpion
57 wear a kilt
58 win a bet
59 wind a reel of thread
60 write a poem

Tense, aspect, voice

Exercise 24

Change the sentences below in the way indicated by the detailed instructions. Against each new sentence, provide one or more of the following labels for the new verb phrase you have formed:

present (ie *present tense*)	perf. (ie *perfective*)
past (ie *past tense*)	prog. (ie *progressive*)
M (ie *modal*)	pass. (ie *passive*)

A *Rephrase, with the verb in the passive*

1 You never take me to a restaurant.
2 We choose you as our spokesman.
3 They don't sell this drug without a prescription.
4 Somebody shut the door in my face.
5 The dog bit several people badly.
6 I must do this exercise again.
7 We can see the signal clearly from here.
8 Nobody could beat him in those days.
9 The municipality is building two new bridges.
10 They were driving the cattle into trucks.
11 Someone has eaten all the bread.
12 The storm had sunk two of our boats.

B *Rephrase, with the verb in the progressive*

13 I sit here by myself all day long.
14 My father ages rapidly.
15 It rained hard during the night.
16 You told us about your engagement.
17 I have bought some presents for the children.
18 The plane had flown too low.

C *Rephrase, with the verb in the perfective*

19 He sleeps through every lecture.
20 You never show any interest.
21 I never met her before then.
22 The meeting began before my arrival.
23 She must be very unhappy.
24 I could find it easily yesterday.

Question tags and contracted forms

Exercise 25

Supply an appropriate question tag for each of the sentences below, as in the model. For the negative, use the contracted form. When alternative forms, eg *haven't* and *don't* are acceptable, give both forms.

Model:
It's very cold today, isn't it?

1 We're not too late,
2 I'm coming with you,
3 You understand what I'm saying,
4 He's doing his best,
5 He's done his best,
6 He has enough money,
7 He usually has three lumps of sugar,
8 There's not enough bread,
9 There's not been a mistake,
10 You can see what is happening,
11 You saw what happened,
12 We all had a good time,
13 You'll be quite all right,
14 There won't be any difficulty,
15 You'd be more comfortable here,
16 You'd been up since five o'clock,
17 We'd set out tomorrow if we could,
18 You'd set out too late and missed the train,
19 You didn't set out till after eight o'clock,
20 We need not do any more,

DO

Exercise 26

Indicate, by the symbol *a, b,* or *c,* etc. whether DO in the following sentences is used as

a a lexical verb
b an interrogative operator
c a negative operator
d an emphatic affirmative
e an emphatic imperative
f a pro-form

A Do[1] do[2] me a favour.
B How do[1] you do[2]?
C I do[1] know you did[2] your best.
D I don't[1] smoke, and nor does[2] Henry.
E Don't[1] do[2] that, please!
F A Did[1] you tell me you'd be away?
  B Of course I did[2].
G A You forgot to post that letter, didn't[1] you?
  B But I did[2] post it.
H I didn't[1] do[2] any damage.
I Do[1] that again. I didn't[2] see it properly.
J Do[1] stop! You know it annoys me, don't[2] you?

Dynamic and stative verbs

Exercise 27

Indicate, by a symbol *a, b* or *c,* etc., whether the verbs in the sentences below express

a an activity
b a process that someone or something can undergo
c a bodily sensation that someone experiences

d a transitional event
e a series of momentary acts
f inert perception or cognition
g a relationship.

A As soon as I know[1], I'll ring[2] you up.
B Somebody is waiting[1] to speak[2] to me.
C I think[1] this meat has gone[2] bad.
D You're forgetting[1] everything I told[2] you.
E I heard[1] that dog barking[2] all night.
F I can't walk[1] any farther. My leg is hurting[2] badly.
G Please stop[1]. You're hurting[2] my leg.
H We consider[1] that the situation has become[2] too serious.
I We must consider[1] carefully how to proceed.[2]
J I've weighed[1] your suitcase. It weighs[2] 22 kilos.
K Does this rule apply[1] to everyone who applies[2] for this post?
L Would you like[1] to taste[2] this wine?
M Tell[1] me if it tastes[2] too sweet.
N We grow[1] our own vegetables and always have[2] enough.
O As we grow[1] older, we become[2] absent-minded.
P I can't remember[1] who this belongs[2] to.
Q We're landing[1]. Fasten[2] your seat belt.
R Feel[1] that radiator. Does it feel[2] very hot?
S I'm getting[1] tired. Would you get[2] me a chair?
T A The city extends[1] for miles and miles.
B Yes, and they're extending[2] it all the time.

Progressive aspect, present

Exercise 28

Write either the simple or the progressive form of the verb in brackets, as you consider appropriate. Use only the present tense and non-perfective aspect:

1 A Where are you?
B I'm upstairs. I (have) a bath.
2 I (have) something to say to you.
3 Hurry up. The train (just come) in.
4 The Nile (flow) into the Mediterranean.
5 We must take an umbrella. It (rain).
6 Wood usually (float) on water.
7 Look out! The ceiling (fall) in!
8 Six times sixteen (equal) ninety six.
9 A What's the matter? Why the train (stop)?
B Because the signal is against us.
10 A I (realize) I should not have said that.
B That's all right. I (forgive) you.

11 The Committee is still in session. It (consider) what action to take next.
12 The Manager can't see you now. He (have) a visitor.
13 He can't see you now. He (dictate) letters.
14 My elder brother is a truck driver. He (drive) those enormous juggernauts.
15 Don't talk to me. I (try) to learn this page by heart.
16 A Call a doctor quickly! The old man (die).
B The doctor is on his way. He (just leave) his house.
17 It's too late. Nothing (matter) now.
18 Don't be upset. I (understand) perfectly.

Progressive aspect, past

Exercise 29

Write either the simple or the progressive form, as appropriate. Use only the past tense, non-perfective aspect:

1 She's alive! She (drown) but that handsome young man (dive) in and (save) her, just in time.
2 I (listen) to the radio when you (ring) the bell the first time, and that's why I (not hear) you.
3 The first plane (explode) just as our plane (land), but our pilot skilfully (climb) up again before touching the tarmac. All the people who (wait) for us (witness) the incident.
4 I'm afraid there's no more bread. We (eat) it all last night. In any case, it (go) stale.
5 While the train (still move), a great many men suddenly (jump) out. I (think) that something terrible (happen), so I (run) away.
6 At school, we (study) two foreign languages.
7 As a boy, I (always read) – I always (have) my nose in a book.
8 A young lady (leave) this note for you ten minutes ago. As you (have) breakfast, I (not disturb) you at the time.

Progressive, present perfect

Exercise 30

Write either the non-progressive or the progressive form of the present perfect, as appropriate:

1 I (know) Miss Huggins for several years. I (read) her latest novel, but I (not finish) it yet.
2 This is the third time you (be) here. What exactly (you come) for now?
3 John (learn) English for seven years, and at last he (master) the irregular verbs.
4 It (rain) but it (stop) now.
5 I (remember) his name. It's Covington.

Progressive or non-progressive

Exercise 31

In many cases, either the non-progressive or the progressive form of the verb may be used. The choice may depend on where the speaker or writer decides to put a special emphasis. Indicate by *Yes* or *No* whether the verbs underlined in the passages below could, in the context, be properly changed from non-progressive to progressive, or vice-versa:

1 Next day we were sitting[a] in the car outside the house, when up the road came[b] a tall lean man.

2 What I can't understand is why, as he was leaving[a], I said[b] to him, 'Good-bye, sir'.

3 A friend of mine went[a] to call on him the morning after his arrival and asked[b] him how he was and whether he was enjoying[c] himself. The visitor said[d] he was feeling[e] well, but he had had[f] a frightening experience earlier that morning. He had gone[g], he said[h], to the railway station. He said[i], 'I stood[j] by an iron gate to watch a train come in, when this frightening thing happened[k]. As the train came[l] nearer and nearer to where I stood[m], all the doors at one moment swung[n] outward, and while the train was still moving[o] a great many men jumped[p] out, quite silently, and began[q] to run towards me.'

4 It was in the South Atlantic on a dark and cloudy afternoon in 1848. The *Daedulus* was ploughing[a] through a long ocean swell. The Commander was pacing[b] the quarterdeck. Another officer, named Sartoris, was keeping[c] watch from the bridge. Sartoris suddenly pointed[d] to a strange object approaching them. It was moving[e] fairly rapidly towards the ship and soon became[f] clearly visible.

5 I jumped[a] up at the sound. I recall[b], now, an awareness that I was being[c] foolish.

Exercise 32

Examine the five passages in Exercise 31 again, and say (a) why in some cases no change in the verb form would be acceptable, (b) why in other cases a change could be made, and (c) if a change could be made, what difference in emphasis would result.

Simple past *or* present perfect

Exercise 33

Write either the simple past or the present perfect form of the verbs in brackets, as appropriate:

1 We (live) in this house since 1970; that is to say, ever since my father (die). He (come) to this country twenty years ago. He (be) born in South America, and (live) there until he (get) married.

2 Although we (be) in this village six years so far, we (not get) to know many people yet. But our next door neighbours (be) very helpful when we first (move) in.
3 I (receive) John's invitation yesterday, and (accept) it at once: I (not see) him for several weeks.
4 That man (catch) any fish yet? I (watch) him for the last hour and he (not move) once.
5 Quick! There (be) an accident. Phone the hospital. The accident (happen) when that red car (shoot) out of the side street without warning.
6 A Why are the flags at half-mast?
B General Hopkins (die). He (never recover) from that last operation.

Past perfect

Exercise 34

Supply the past perfect when necessary; otherwise the simple past:

1 A I (see) John in the park yesterday.
B How (be) he?
A Very well. He (be) ill and (be) in bed for almost three weeks, but he (have) a few days' convalescence by the sea.
B He (start) work again?
A No, not yet. He'll start again on Monday.
2 After a long forced march, Caesar (enter) the town only to find that the enemy (flee): he (make) the long march in vain.
3 Columbus (gaze) at the land that he (come) so far to seek: he (see) nothing but ocean for five long weeks.
4 The fire (sweep) across the prairie and (approach) within a few miles of the fort. Fields, which (lie) parched throughout the summer, (blaze) for a few seconds and (be) left blackened and smouldering.
5 We (go) out into the streets. Fierce fighting (take) place all around us, but now all (be) quiet again.

Simple past *or* past perfect

Exercise 35

Indicate by *Yes* or *No* whether the verbs underlined in the passages below could be properly changed from simple past to past perfect, or vice-versa.

1 We arrived after the ship sailed[a], and when our heavy luggage had already been put[b] on board.
2 The manager of the Court Theatre put on a play that failed[a]; the next play he had arranged[b] to put on was not ready. So I offered[c] him a play of mine called *Lady Frederick*.
3 The family had retired[a] for the night when I arrived[b], wet and cold. The butler, who explained[c] that I had not been expected[d] so soon, showed[e] me my room, and my bed, but I could not occupy the latter as my predecessor had not yet vacated[f] it.

4 Many years before, the beautiful wife of an Indian chief, to whom she had been[a] unfaithful, climbed[b] up to this lonely spot and drowned[c] herself in the lake.
5 An official called Hsieh Wei had been lying[a] sick for many days, when he fell[b] into a feverish doze.
6 As a boy he had been[a] fond of swimming, but now he was[b] out of practice.
7 The ancient Greeks could rightly boast that every contemporary civilization on the face of the planet (whose shape and size they had accurately calculated[a]) had been penetrated[b] by their world-conquering culture.

Future

Exercise 36

Indicate by *a, b, c, d, e, f, g, h, i,* whether future reference can be made through the verbs in brackets by

a will + infinitive
b shall + infinitive
c BE going to + infinitive
d will be *-ing*
e shall be *-ing*
f the present progressive
g the simple present
h BE to + infinitive
i BE about to + infinitive

Your answer may consist of two or more of those symbols.

1 I (live) on a desert island, where there (be) no telephone, and I (have) the satisfaction of knowing that the telephone (never ring) and I (never have) to answer it.
2 Most areas (have) rain tomorrow, and there (be) thundery showers in many places.
3 We (find) a cure for cancer one day; but in the meantime this awful disease (claim) thousands of victims a year.
4 You say that production (be) much lower this year. But if you (go) into any factory in this region, you (hear) quite a different story.
5 A You've spilt some coffee down your dress. It (leave) a stain.
B It (leave) a stain unless I (clean) it at once.
A I have some CLEENIT. Rub that on right away, and the stain (come) out all right.
B Thanks. Yes, it's coming out. It (do) the trick.
6 If you (swim) this afternoon, you shouldn't eat too much now.
7 If you (swim) this afternoon, be very careful of the current.
8 A I expect Friday's meeting (be) a long one: we (discuss) next year's budget.
B Yes. I imagine we (be) here till eight o'clock.
9 A The Professor (be) very busy tomorrow. He (give) two lectures in the morning, then he (go) to York for a conference.
B What time he (leave) for York?

A He (catch) the 12.15 train and (get) to York just after three.
B So he (be) pretty tired by the time he (get) back.

10 Watch carefully now. I (show) you one of the most remarkable photographs ever taken.
11 You (get) up today, or you (stay) in bed? If you (get) up, don't go outside. It (be) very cold.
12 The Prime Minister (be) guest of honour at a dinner given by the Press Association this evening. About a hundred guests (be) present.
13 A Listen to this. 'The new bridge across the Ouse (be opened) officially on June 30th, but (not be) accessible to motorists for another six weeks.'
B That means we (keep) off it for another two months at least.

Future-in-the-past

Exercise 37

Indicate, by *a, b, c, d, e* or *f,* whether reference to future time in the past can be made through the verbs in brackets by

a would + infinitive	d the past progressive
b should + ,,	e was or were to + infinitive
c was or were going to + infinitive	f was or were about to + infinitive

Your answer may consist of more than one symbol.

1 The weather forecast yesterday said that many areas (have) rain, but we certainly didn't have any here.
2 I warned you not to eat so much lunch if you (swim) yesterday afternoon.
3 It was 1491. Columbus (discover) America in the following year.
4 A Do you know where Professor X is?
B I know he (catch) the 12.15 train for York, where he (attend) a conference.
5 I (show) you that photograph when I was interrupted.
6 The Prime Minister, who (be) guest of honour at the Press Association dinner, left his office at 7.30 precisely.
7 My instructions were that motorists (not use) the new bridge yet.
8 We knew that Friday's meeting (be) a long one, as we (discuss) the budget.

Subjunctive

Exercise 38

Indicate, by *a, b, c, d* or *e,* whether the verbs underlined provide examples of

a the mandative subjunctive
b the formulaic ,,
c the <u>were</u> ,,
d the modal past
or e a normal use of the indicative mood

1 I suggest that you <u>were feeling</u> over-tired.
2 We suggest that this applicant apply next year.

3 If I were feeling over-tired, I wouldn't go on.
4 I would much rather we stayed at home this evening.
5 We were hoping you could come and have lunch with us tomorrow.
6 The Committee recommends that the annual subscription be increased to £3.
7 It is highly desirable that every effort be made to reduce expenditure and that every member of the staff economize wherever possible.
8 Be that as it may, our expenditure is bound to increase.
9 By the time we stopped, we had driven six hundred miles.
10 Is it not time we set our own house in order?

Modals

Exercise 39

Replace each of the passages underlined by the appropriate modal auxiliary + lexical verb:

1 John is capable of typing very fast.
2 I know how to answer this question now.
3 I was never able to understand a word he said.
4 No one was able to solve the problem.
5 It is just possible that what you say is true.
6 I suggest I open the window.
7 If you are willing to come with us, we shall be delighted.
8 Would you like to have a seat?
9 Someone keeps putting his coat on my peg.
10 Grandfather has got into the habit of sitting looking at this view all day long.
11 I had a habit of hitting the wrong key of the typewriter.
12 Grandfather had got into the habit of sitting in that chair for hours.
13 I advise you to read this book.
14 It is obligatory for us to read it.
15 You are prohibited from smoking here.
16 Are you able to do this without help?
17 Is it advisable for us to wait?
18 It is not compulsory for us to attend.
19 That, presumably, is the house we're looking for.
20 Yes, I'm quite sure that it is the one.

Exercise 40

Rewrite the following as past reported speech, beginning each sentence with *I said that*:

1 John can type very fast.
2 You can go if you want to.
3 I may be late home.

4 If you will come with us, we shall be delighted.
5 Someone will keep putting his coat on my peg.
6 You should read this book.
7 Everyone must read it.
8 We needn't attend that lecture.
9 That house will be the one we're looking for.
10 That must be the one.

Exercise 41

Imagine that *today* in each of the following sentences is changed to *yesterday*, and give the form of the modal that would then be required. Note that action unfulfilled is implied in sentences 2, 5, 6 and 7.

1 You can pronounce this word perfectly today.
2 You may stay at home today.
3 The Minister must speak on that subject today.
4 No one dare go out into the streets today.
5 I can let you have the money today, if you want it.
6 You should read this book today.
7 I could go with you today.
8 It must be very hot in town today.
9 There might be too much traffic on the roads today.
10 He will do anything for me today.

Exercise 42

Indicate which of the modal auxiliaries could replace the one underlined, without change of meaning. If no replacement is possible, write *None*. If the modal can be omitted, write *Zero*.

1 Can I borrow your pen please?
2 I may be late home tonight.
3 I could never play the banjo properly.
4 We might go to the concert if there's time.
5 We shall let you know our decision soon.
6 The vendor shall maintain the equipment in good repair.
7 Shall I come with you?
8 Will you have a piece of cake?
9 Would you mind shutting the door?
10 You should do as he says.
11 It is odd that you should say that.
12 We should love to go abroad.
13 If you should change your mind, please let us know.
14 If you would change this book, I should be very grateful.

15 If there were a fire, I know what I <u>should</u> do, but I'm not sure what I <u>would</u> do.
16 You <u>ought</u> to see him act.
17 There <u>may</u> have been an accident.
18 You <u>must</u> be more careful.

Exercise 43

Each of the following is ambiguous by itself. Paraphrase each sentence, in two different ways, so as to show the difference in possible interpretations:

1 Henry can drive my car now.
2 Anyone can make mistakes.
3 We could go to the theatre.
4 You may be out late this evening.
5 I should be pleased to see him.
6 They should be home now.
7 You will sit there.
8 You must be very quick.
9 The guests will have arrived.
10 Shall we see him this evening?

Exercise 44

Give a response, on one of the following models, to each of the stimuli given below, using the modal in brackets:

Models:
A I'm not listening. (should)
B Then you should be listening.
A I think I lost it. (must)
B Yes, you must have lost it.

A I didn't hear it. (should)
B But you should have heard it.
A You were dreaming. (must)
B Yes, I must have been dreaming.

1 A He's probably coming. (may)
B Yes,
2 A He has probably arrived. (may)
B Yes,
3 A You didn't remember it. (could)
B No,
4 A You have been mistaken. (may)
B Yes,
5 A Perhaps he was asleep. (might)
B Yes,
6 A Or perhaps he was only dozing. (must)
B Yes,
7 A I wasn't attending. (ought to)
B Then
8 A I haven't finished. (ought to)
B But
9 A He was smoking. (ought not to)
B Then
10 A He didn't see the notice. (should)
B Well,
11 A I expect he is there by now. (will)
B Yes,
12 A He's got there by now. (will)
B I agree,
13 A They were probably having dinner. (would)
B Yes,
14 A They didn't hear me. (could)
B No,
15 A I think you were mistaken. (might)
B Yes,
16 A You were mistaken. (can't)
B No,

4 The noun phrase

Determiners

Exercise 45

Complete the table below. See the note in the instructions to Exercise 20.

Determiner	*Count, singular*	*Count, plural*	*Non-Count*	*Pronominal*
a(n)	book	—	—	one
any (unstressed)	—	books	money	any
any (stressed)				
each				
either				
enough				
every				
my				
neither				
much				
no				
some (unstressed)				
some (stressed)				
that				
the				
this				
these				
those				
what				
which				
whose				
zero				

Predeterminers

Exercise 46

Which of the three predeterminers *all, both* and *half* could acceptably replace X as predeterminers? Note that more than one answer may be acceptable.

1 I have read X of this book already.
2 I have read X of these books already.
3 X the students were away.
4 X students were too ill to get up.
5 X had influenza.
6 They X had a high fever.
7 X of them had to go to hospital.
8 X the medicine they took was no use.
9 It X cost a lot of money.
10 They were X away for weeks.
11 Doctor Bland attended them X.
12 He visited X of them every day.
13 He was sometimes up X the night.
14 Once or twice he was up X night.
15 The patients have X recovered.

Quantifiers

Exercise 47

Complete the table below to illustrate the co-occurrence of *quantifiers with count nouns, singular and plural, and with non-count nouns.* See the note in the instructions to Exercise 20.

Quantifier	*Count, plural*	*Non-count*	*Pronominal*
a large amount of			
a great deal of			
enough	books	money	enough
(a) few			
(a) little			
a lot of			
much			
a large number of			
plenty of			
several			

Generic or specific reference

Exercise 48

Write *gen.* or *spec.* to indicate whether the noun underlined has *generic* or *specific reference:*

1 The pen[a] is mightier than the sword[b].
2 The pen I bought yesterday has broken already.
3 There is a cat on the roof.
4 A cat is a small domestic animal.
5 Cats have been domesticated for centuries.
6 There were cats everywhere.
7 The Japanese work very hard.
8 The Japanese were listening patiently.
9 The Welsh love to sing in chorus.
10 The Welshmen were singing lustily.

Exercise 49

Replace *Switzerland* in the first sentence of the passage below by the names of twelve different countries and make other changes that will then be necessary in the remaining sentences.

My friend comes from Switzerland. He is a Swiss and speaks with a charming Swiss accent. There are two compatriots of his – two other Swiss – staying with him. The Swiss are very friendly people.

Articles

Exercise 50

Write *a, an, the* or *O,* according to which article is required at the point indicated by the oblique stroke. If there are two possible answers, give them both.

1 /[a] men used to live in /[b] caves but /[c] few people make homes in them now.

2 /[a] beacon was /[b] light or fire used as /[c] signal to give warning of /[d] danger.

3 /[a] beacons are now placed on /[b] top of /[c] mountains or on /[d] rock in /[e] sea to guide /[f] planes or /[g] ships.

4 To grow /[a] corn, /[b] farmers sow /[c] seed in /[d] spring. That is /[e] season when many trees are in /[f] flower.

5 /[a] fruit ripens in /[b] autumn and then /[c] leaves of /[d] certain trees fall.

6 /[a] summer is /[b] warmest season, but /[c] summer of 1971 was unusually cool.

7 /[a] chief occupation of /[b] population of /[c] India is /[d] agriculture. /[e] India's population is enormous, and /[f] large part of it still works in /[g] fields.

8 /[a] last week we performed /[b] experiment to see how /[c] rust forms on /[d] metal. We dipped /[e] pieces of /[f] iron in /[g] water and left them for /[h] half /[i] hour. Then we examined them under /[j] microscope. After /[k] few days, /[l] rust had become quite thick.

9 /[a] wild animals never kill for /[b] sport. /[c] man is /[d] only animal to whom /[e] torture and /[f] death of his fellow-creatures is amusing.

10 /[a] half of /[b] world cannot understand /[c] pleasures of /[d] other.

11 I want /[a] information about /[b] latest developments in /[c] cancer research.

12 /[a] first article in /[b] *English Journal* is interesting, /[c] arguments in it are sound, but /[d] statements in /[e] third paragraph are not entirely accurate, and /[f] figures are out of /[g] date.

13 What would you like for /[a] breakfast? /[b] eggs and /[c] bacon? /[d] tea or /[e] coffee?

14 I don't eat much in /[a] morning. If I have /[b] big breakfast all I need for /[c] lunch is /[d] salad and /[e] glass of /[f] milk.

15 If I have /[a] big supper, I can't sleep at /[b] night.

16 Long before the birth of /[a] Christopher Columbus, /[b] people in /[c] Europe believed that /[d] land of /[e] plenty, with /[f] perfect climate, lay to /[g] west across /[h] Atlantic Ocean.

17 /[a] Aswan Dam holds back /[b] flood waters of /[c] Blue Nile and /[d] Atbara.

18 /[a] Japanese use /[b] same kind of /[c] writing as /[d] Chinese.
19 /[a] London University has /[b] more students than /[c] University of /[d] Oxford. Many of /[e] students at /[f] former study at /[g] home or in /[h] British Museum.
20 I believe /[a] souls of /[b] five hundred Sir Isaac Newtons would go to /[c] making of /[d] Shakespeare or /[e] Milton.
21 /[a] object of /[b] government in /[c] peace and /[d] war is not /[e] glory of /[f] rulers or of /[g] races but /[h] happiness of /[i] common man.
22 One day, about /[a] noon, /[b] Robinson Crusoe was surprised to see /[c] print of /[d] man's naked foot on /[e] shore. He could see it very clearly in /[f] sand.
23 /[a] medicine can be unpleasant, even dangerous. /[b] remedy can be worse than /[c] disease: it can cure /[d] disease and kill /[e] patient.
24 /[a] little fire burns up /[b] great deal of /[c] corn.
25 /[a] Andrew is studying /[b] Roman law at /[c] University and /[d] Paul is doing /[e] research in either /[f] sixteenth century literature, or /[g] literature of /[h] early renaissance – I don't know which.
26 I am going to /[a] town by /[b] bus and coming back on /[c] train. I'll come by /[d] 2.15 train, I think.
27 John Smart was trained as /[a] lawyer. Then he took up /[b] politics and was returned as /[c] member of /[d] parliament. He was appointed /[e] junior minister in /[f] White administration, and was later made /[g] Minister of /[h] Interior.
28 We went on /[a] board /[b] *Canton* in /[c] evening and sailed during /[d] night. We were then at /[e] sea for six weeks: that is why we were away at /[f] Christmas and /[g] New Year.
29 My brother has /[a] very good job. He is /[b] Director of /[c] department in /[d] new factory down by /[e] sea, with /[f] seat on /[g] board.
30 /[a] love of /[b] money is /[c] root of all /[d] evil.

Nouns ending in *s*

Exercise 51

Put into the *singular* as many of the nouns in the following sentences as can be used in the singular in the context, and make other changes that then become necessary:

1 The Middle Ages were times of feudal rivalries.
2 The drivers must produce their certificates to the customs.
3 The soldiers left their arms in the barracks.
4 Barracks are buildings used as military quarters.
5 Goods trains carry heavier loads than trucks do.

Concord between subject and verb

Exercise 52

Make the right concord between subject and verb by selecting one member of each of the pairs of verbs in the following sentences:

1 There {is / are} people waiting to see you.

2 The people wholeheartedly {support / supports} you.

3 Ours {is / are} a great people, {isn't it / aren't they} ?

4 The police {has / have} an unenviable task.

5 You old folk {doesn't / don't} know anything about us.

6 Splendid cattle {was / were} grazing on the hillside.

7 The youth {is / are} more serious than my generation was.

8 The youth {was / were} more serious than his uncle.

9 The news, I'm afraid, {has / have} got much worse.

10 Mumps {is / are} an unpleasant ailment.

11 Linguistics {has / have} developed rapidly in modern times.

12 The acoustics of this hall {is / are} excellent.

13 The archives of this society {is / are} kept in the basement.

14 {Do / Does} people always believe what you say?

15 Bacteria of the harmful kind {cause / causes} disease.

Plural of nouns

Exercise 53

Put into the plural as many of the nouns in the following sentences as will take a plural form, and make other changes that then become necessary.

1 A crisis often occurs in the best regulated family.
2 Another criterion is needed in analysing this phenomenon.
3 The anonymous workman was the real hero on the campus.
4 The runner-up was given a pound note.
5 The skeleton found in the lower stratum was taken at once to the museum.

Exercise 54

Check the pronunciation and spelling of the plural of:

album
appendix
basis
branch
breakdown
bureau
chassis
chorus
church
concerto
country
diagnosis
diploma
echo
fish
foot
formula
fox
gentleman
goose
half
handkerchief
house
index
key
knee
knife
lady
larva
lay-by
leaf
lens
loaf
man-of-war
month
mouse
mouth
niece
onlooker
ovum
passer-by
penny
photo
potato
rat
salmon
series
sheep
shelf
sister-in-law
spoonful
stimulus
syllabus
tooth
ultimatum
village
volcano
wife
wolf
woman

Gender

Exercise 55

Replace X in the following sentences by either *who* or *which,* Y by either *he, she* or *it,* and Z by either *his, her, its* or *their*. If two (or more) answers are possible, give them both (or all):

1 I know a man X could help you. Y is very kind.
2 I have a friend X could help you. Y is very kind.
3 I have an aunt X could tell you, but Y is rather a bore.
4 My neighbour, X is an expert on such matters, will tell you, but Y is out at the moment.
5 The Committee, X meets every Wednesday, has not yet made up Z mind.
6 The Committee, X are very sympathetic, are giving the matter Z careful consideration.
7 The group X dominated society then was the family. Y continued to do so for centuries.
8 The family, X were seriously worried, met to discuss the scandal. Y decided to try to hush it up.
9 The baby, X had fallen out of Z perambulator, continued to scream as loudly as Y could.
10 The poor bitch, with Z five puppies, lay shivering in the corner. Y showed no inclination to move.
11 The majority, X are in favour of the new measures, want to make Z voices heard.
12 Japan, X was isolated from the rest of the world for nearly three hundred years, has now taken Z place as a member of a world community.

The genitive with apostrophe *s*

Exercise 56

Paraphrase the phrases below by means of a noun modified by a relative clause, as in the model.

Model: John's hat – the hat that John has.

1 John's story
2 John's present
3 John's mistake
4 John's punishment
5 John's supper
6 His father's consent
7 His father's interest
8 His father's conclusion
9 His father's influence
10 His uncle's murder

The genitive with *'s* or with *of*

Exercise 57

Write the form of the genitive (ie with *'s* or *of*) which could be related to the following sentences. If two forms are possible, give them both. One example is given as a guide.

	Genitive
1 John has a brother.	John's brother.
2 Thomas has a sister.	
3 Sophocles wrote plays.	
4 Keats wrote poetry.	
5 The cow gives milk.	
6 The captain made an error.	
7 The ship has a siren.	
8 The siren made a noise.	
9 Somebody has a hat.	
10 Something has a name.	
11 The school has a history.	
12 The world has problems.	
13 Europe has art treasures.	
14 The holiday lasted a week.	
15 The work took a year.	
16 My brother-in-law has a house.	
17 My parents gave their consent.	
18 The man over there has a name.	
19 This book has pages.	
20 The newspaper published this evening.	

The double genitive

Exercise 58

Form a sentence with double genitive, if one can be formed acceptably, from the following material:

1 John is one of my friends.
2 One of Doctor Black's patients has died.
3 That dog – Jack's dog – has torn my trousers.
4 Where is that key, the one you have?

5 Where is the key, the one you have?
6 Those new shoes, I mean yours, look very smart.
7 This is Doctor Black's secretary.
8 This book, John Christie's, is very amusing.
9 That is a tale told by an idiot.
10 These exercises you set are quite easy.

Personal, reflexive and possessive pronouns

Exercise 59

Supply a personal, reflexive or possessive pronoun to replace each of the dashes in the passages below. Each passage is a continuous context.

1 This is my property. $_a$______ is $_b$______ own. $_c$______ bought $_d$______. $_e$______ paid for $_f$______ out of $_g$______ own money, so $_h$______ is $_i$______.
2 One must take care of $_a$______ own property and look after $_b$______ $_c$______. If you keep an animal, $_d$______ must look after $_e$______ properly: $_f$______ cannot always look after $_g$______.
3 $_a$______ think of myself too much. My mother thinks of $_b$______ as well and often forgets to think of $_c$______.
4 They must do $_a$______ duty, as we must do $_b$______. We have kept $_c$______ promise: let them keep $_d$______.
5 She knows $_a$______ own mind but he doesn't know $_b$______ own at all. He loses $_c$______ temper, while $_d$______ always keeps $_e$______. She keeps $_f$______ under perfect control; but $_g$______ can't control himself.
6 Every country has $_a$______ own traditions, and prides $_b$______ on $_c$______. We must all maintain those traditions and pass $_d$______ on to $_e$______ children.
7 Do you see that flower in front of $_a$______? You recognize $_b$______? Then tell $_c$______ $_d$______ name.

Exercise 60

Replace each of the bracketed parts of the sentences below by an appropriate personal or reflexive pronoun:

1 John and Mary said they would go out by (John and Mary).
2 Mary assured John that she could look after (Mary).
3 John told Mary that he would look after (Mary).
4 You, Mary, will have to look after (Mary).
5 Can you and Mary look after (you and Mary)?
6 Can you and Mary get supper for (you, Mary and me)?
7 Can you, Mary and I get supper for (you, Mary and me)?
8 One must learn to look after (one) these days.
9 No one should deceive (no one) about that.
10 I have just been out to get (me) a cup of coffee.

11 Many people believe (many people) to be chosen vessels.
12 Everybody clings to this illusion about (everybody).
13 The Romans eventually had enemies all about (the Romans).
14 If we look around (we), we see that we are just as other men are.
15 Alexander always kept a faithful friend beside (Alexander).
16 When he found that he had been betrayed, he was beside (him) with fury.

Relative pronouns

Exercise 61

Indicate whether the relative pronoun at X can be *that, what, which, who, whom, whose* or *0* (zero). If two or more answers are possible, give them both or all.

1 The world X he entered was a strange one.
2 He took two rooms for X he paid £5 a week.
3 The theatre X he usually went to was the Royal.
4 He wrote several novels, only one of X had any merit.
5 The man X spoke to me just now is an astronaut.
6 The man X you were just speaking to is his brother.
7 He is a man about X very little is known.
8 The man X brother is an astronaut is leaving.
9 X was discovered was an almost impregnable city.
10 The people X built such a refuge must have been very ingenious.

What, which, whom or whose

Exercise 62

Indicate whether the interrogative word at X can be *what, which, who, whom* or *whose*. If two answers are possible, give them both.

1 If you had to live alone on a desert island, X would you take with you?
2 If you had to choose between a flute and a violin, X instrument would you prefer?
3 X was it that said, 'To be, or not to be'?
4 X of Shakespeare's plays have you read?
5 X of the characters in *War and Peace* do you find the most interesting?
6 X modern novels have you read recently?
7 If that is not your essay, then X is it?
8 X man could possibly behave like that?
9 X have I the honour of addressing?
10 To X and to X department should my application be submitted?

Each, every

Exercise 63

Indicate whether the dash in each of the sentences below can be replaced by *each* or *every*. If either word is acceptable, give them both.

1 ______ man in the crowd raised his hand.
2 There were police on ______ side of the square.
3 The crowd lined ______ side of the street.
4 ______ one of the two men was six feet tall.
5 ______ one in the team received a prize.
6 ______ received a medal, too.
7 The ceremony will be repeated ______ two years.
8 The players received £100 ______.
9 They ______ received a bonus.
10 They were ______ looking anxiously at the referee.

Universal and partitive pronouns and determiners

Exercise 64

Choose one item from the left-hand column to replace each dash in the sentences below:

all
any
anyone
anything
anywhere
each
either
every
everyone
everything
everywhere
it all
neither
no
no one
none
nothing
nowhere
some
someone
something
somewhere
them all
they all

1 I haven't read all of this book but I've read $_a$______ of it. At least I know $_b$______ about the subject.
2 I haven't read $_a$______ of the last four chapters yet, so I know $_b$______ about them, I'm afraid.
3 It is a big book, but we're expected to read $_a$______ during the year. We can't leave $_b$______ out.
4 A I can't find my pen $_a$______. I've looked $_b$______ for it.
5 B But it must be $_a$______. Where haven't you looked?
A $_b$______.
6 Has smoking $_a$______ to do with cancer? $_b$______ people believe smoking has $_c$______ to do with cancer at all. Others feel that it might have $_d$______ to do with it, but they don't know what.
7 Is $_a$______ of the increase due to better diagnosis? Yes, $_b$______ of it undoubtedly is: one could not pretend that $_c$______ of it is.
8 $_a$______ doctors insist that $_b$______ should give up smoking. Do you think that $_c$______ need give it up? I think that $_d$______ people ought to, but not $_e$______.
9 A Here are two keys. Will $_a$______ of them fit this drawer?
B No, $_b$______ of them will. There is in fact $_c$______ key for that drawer.
10 $_a$______ man in the village assembled to hear the verdict. $_b$______ came; and the verdict was announced to $_c$______.

Some and *any* with assertion, non-assertion

Exercise 65

Identify the *non-assertive* component in each of the following sentences:

1 There isn't anything we can do.
2 We have scarcely any money left.
3 If you need any help, please let me know.
4 I do not believe your intervention will make any difference.
5 We seldom have any occasion for using this expensive machinery.
6 Is there anyone here who speaks Arabic?
7 Before we go any further, we must agree on procedure.
8 Is there anywhere we can go to be really quiet?
9 Unless you have anything more to say, I shall consider the matter closed.
10 A curfew was imposed in an attempt to prevent any further violence.

Terminology

Exercise 66

Give a brief explanation, supported by two illustrations, of each of the following terms as used in *A University Grammar of English*:

1 a determiner
2 a predeterminer
3 cardinal numerals
4 ordinal numerals
5 closed-system quantifiers
6 generic reference
7 specific reference
8 cataphoric reference
9 anaphoric reference
10 summation plurals
11 pluralia tantum in *-s*
12 voicing + *s* plural
13 mutation
14 dual gender
15 common gender
16 double genitive
17 partitive pronouns
18 universal pronouns
19 non-assertion
20 replacive *one*

5 Adjectives and adverbs

Adjective or adverb?

Exercise 67

Indicate by *adj* if the final word of the sentence is an adjective, or by *adv* if it is an adverb:

1 The sun burnt the grass quickly.
2 It burnt the grass black.
3 He drove his employees hard.
4 He drove some of them mad.
5 I find this very unlikely.
6 We found the people friendly.
7 This made everyone late.
8 I have made his acquaintance lately.
9 The doctor soon made the patient well.
10 We can make breakfast early.
11 What made my bed so hard?
12 We shall leave the house early.
13 We shall leave the room empty.
14 I can paint your hall pink.
15 I can paint this wall fast.
16 Pull the rope hard.
17 Pull the rope tight.
18 He turned the corner well.
19 The heat turned the milk sour.
20 You must wipe the windscreen clear.

Adjective phrases

Exercise 68

Rewrite the following sentences, replacing the relative clause in each by an adjective phrase, remembering that such a phrase can be realized by a single word:

1 Will all students who are married please raise their hands?
2 Will all students who are interested write their names on this list.
3 I don't wish to know the names of the people who were involved.
4 All the women who were present looked up in alarm.
5 We should call the doctor who is nearest.
6 We must find the doctor who is concerned.
7 What are the best seats that are available?
8 Can you recommend something that is really interesting?
9 I have a problem that is much more complicated.
10 I have a problem that is much more complicated than that.
11 The road that is best to take is the A 40.

12 The people who are most difficult to understand are often members of one's own family.
13 I have never met a person who was so difficult to understand as my husband.
14 You couldn't find anyone who is more difficult.
15 What I would like to do is to go somewhere where it is really quiet.

Adjective as head of a noun phrase

Exercise 69

Replace the phrase underlined by a noun phrase with an adjective as head, when such replacement is permissible.

1 Robin Hood robbed [a]rich people is order to pay [b]those who were poor.
2 The injured people were conveyed in ambulances to the General Hospital.
3 The injured man lay unattended for several hours.
4 If [a]those who are blind lead [b]others who are blind, both will fall into the ditch.
5 He sat there as silent as if he were a dumb man.
6 Does anyone know the dead man's name?
7 Always speak well of those who have died.
8 I fear he is no longer in the land of those who live.
9 Fear of what is unknown often makes people conservative.
10 Nothing is so certain to happen as something that we do not expect.
11 These seats are reserved for men who have been disabled.
12 The English country gentleman galloping after a fox – [a]what is unspeakable in full pursuit of [b]something he cannot eat.
13 [a]Wise men are often confounded by [b]a foolish man.
14 The nurse sleeps sweetly, hired to watch those who are sick, whom, snoring, she disturbs.
15 Have you heard the latest news?

Verbless adjective clauses

Exercise 70

When it is possible to do so, rewrite the following sentences using a verbless adjective clause.

1 The men were eager to begin the climb and they rose at first light.
2 The summit, which was bare and bleak, towered above them.
3 They studied the cliff face: it was perpendicular.
4 They found a ledge which was narrow enough for one man.
5 They were thoroughly exhausted as they crawled into their sleeping bags.
6 They could hardly stand, as they were stiff in every joint.
7 When the snow was fresh, it afforded no sure foothold.
8 The wind was keen as a razor and drove them back into the shelter of their tent.

9 Though their tent was as light as a feather, somehow it remained firm.
10 The rescue party brought them down to the base camp: they were half-dead with the cold.

Inherent adjectives

Exercise 71

If the adjectives in the following sentences are inherent in the context, say *Yes*; otherwise *No*:

1 A [a]poor man is not necessarily [b]unhappy.
2 The [a]precise answer is not, as it happens, very [b]precise.
3 A [a]strong supporter does not need to be [b]strong.
4 The [a]perfect solution was found by a [b]perfect genius.
5 The [a]main argument is not, of course, the [b]only one.
6 A [a]big eater is quite often a [b]big man.
7 A [a]hard worker may well have a [b]soft heart.
8 A [a]criminal lawyer does not usually have a [b]criminal record.
9 A [a]complete victory may be won by a [b]complete rogue.
10 A [a]certain friend of mine is by no means [b]certain of the outcome of the negotiations.
11 The people [a]present are waiting for the result of the [b]present talks.
12 Men who spend days in a [a]lunar module are [b]real heroes.

Categories of adjective

Exercise 72

Classify the adjectives as used in the following phrases by putting the number of the phrase in the appropriate frame below:

1 a true scholar
2 the chief reason
3 afraid of mice
4 utter stupidity
5 my entire salary
6 very unwell
7 a healthy man
8 the principal cause
9 a clear road
10 a medical school
11 a possible friend
12 a possible reason
13 a faint impression
14 feeling faint
15 pure water
16 a particular place
17 fond of icecream
18 the late President
19 my old grandfather
20 the solar system

Attributive only

A *Intensifiers*

B *Limiters*

C ***Related to adverbials***

D ***Denominal***

E ***Predicative only***

F ***Central***

Dynamic and gradable adjectives

Exercise 73

Copy out the tables below and use them to classify the adjectives listed, putting a tick (√) in the *a* column if the adjective can be dynamic, a dash(–) if it cannot be, and so on:

a = 'dynamic', as in He is being careless.
b = 'gradable', as in He is very tall.
c = 'subjective', as in He is most annoying.
d = 'negative', as in He is utterly wrong.

	a	b	c	d
1 greedy				
2 asleep				
3 heavy				
4 kind				
5 lazy				
6 stupid				
7 thin				
8 generous				
9 buddhist				
10 early				

	a	b	c	d
11 married				
12 obstinate				
13 new				
14 separate				
15 deaf				
16 tactful				
17 interesting				
18 timid				
19 busy				
20 delightful				

Comparison

Exercise 74

Write down, and pronounce, the comparative and superlative of these adjectives:

1 able
2 bored
3 boring
4 clever
5 cruel
6 dear
7 dry
8 fat
9 fertile
10 free
11 frequent
12 gentle
13 healthy
14 narrow
15 obvious
16 real
17 true
18 useful
19 violent
20 well

Participial adjectives

Exercise 75

Indicate by a tick (√), otherwise by a dash (–), if the participles listed below can be

a used as attributive adjectives
b used as predicative adjectives
c modified by *very, too* or *so*

	a	b	c
1 amazing			
2 broken			
3 confused			
4 damaged			
5 damaging			
6 defined			
7 forgotten			
8 furnished			
9 insured			
10 interesting			
11 known			
12 limited			
13 moved			
14 opposed			
15 pleased			
16 surprising			
17 tiring			
18 trained			
19 unsettled			
20 written			

Exercise 76

The participles listed below can all be used as attributive adjectives modified by *very* provided they are compounded with another element, e.g. *good* in *a very good-looking man.* Supply 'another element' that would be acceptable:

1 based
2 behaved
3 built
4 cooked
5 defined
6 disposed
7 dressed
8 educated
9 expected
10 humoured
11 informed
12 kept
13 known
14 lighted
15 made
16 managed
17 shaven
18 thought out
19 used
20 written

Adverbs

Exercise 77

Rephrase the following sentences using an adverb instead of the adjective underlined:

1 John is a very <u>careful</u> driver.
2 Sue has a very <u>good</u> pronunciation of English vowels.
3 Dick's behaviour is more <u>courteous</u> than Bob's.

4 Of the two, Bob is the clearer speaker.
5 Bob is a very much harder worker.
6 Barrington is not nearly such a fast runner.
7 Radford makes a far less scientific approach to his subject.
8 Henrietta is a most brilliant dancer.
9 Last night's play made a considerable impression on me.
10 In an auction, the highest bidder has to pay.
11 Jones is a much more friendly teacher than Johnson.
12 There has been a much more rapid increase in the number of street accidents in the last ten years.

Exercise 78

Identify the adverb(s) in each of the following sentences. Then classify it/them as *A, B, C,* etc: see below. Where there are two adverbs in a sentence, refer to the first as *a*, the second as *b*:

1 Shut the door quickly
2 You are quite right
3 He plays surprisingly well
4 Hardly anyone came
5 It is rather a pity
6 I am right for once
7 His room is right at the end
8 Wait until afterwards
9 Answer me honestly
10 Honestly, I don't know
11 I haven't met him yet
12 Yet I feel I know him
13 I hope to meet him soon, though.
14 We left home so early
15 We are almost at the station
16 That cost almost a pound
17 It's about double the normal price
18 I didn't say anything, naturally
19 He is really very kind
20 In fact, he is quite a nice man

A ***Adjunct***

B ***Modifying an adj.***

C ***Modifying an adv.***

D ***Modifying a prepositional phrase***

E ***Modifying a determiner***

F ***Modifying a noun phrase***

G ***Complement of preposition***

H ***Disjuncts***

I ***Conjuncts***

6 Prepositions

Prepositional phrases and *that*-clauses

Exercise 79

Replace the *that*-clause in each of the following sentences by a *prepositional phrase* without changing the original meaning:

1 I was afraid that I might fall down the ladder.
2 We were amused that you met the Joneses there.
3 I am not aware that I gave you permission to leave.
4 We are quite confident that we shall win.
5 The committee has decided that the matter be dropped.
6 The brothers were determined they would have their revenge.
7 We are grateful (to you) that you have taken an interest in us.
8 No one is sorry that Lawler has resigned.
9 Are you sure that Simon has disappeared?
10 I am not surprised that he has married again.
11 I assure you that I am willing to stand down.
12 The young man convinced everyone that he was innocent.
13 Did anyone inform you that the plans had been changed?
14 I must remind you that you have a responsibility towards your friends.
15 No one told me that there were these problems.

***wh*-clauses and *that*-clauses after a preposition**

Exercise 80

Combine each of the following pairs of sentences so as to form one sentence containing either a *wh*-clause or *the fact* + a *that*-clause, and retaining the words underlined:

1 What will the Government decide? Our plans depend on that.
2 We have never been consulted. Our protest is due to that.
3 His salary has been increased? I was not aware of it.
4 We are spending more than our income. I am fully conscious of it.
5 Why do you want to borrow all that money? I am interested.
6 You want to go to Peru. I am interested.
7 Who is in the audience? Some speakers are very sensitive to that.

8 What started the fire? I am not sure about it.
9 I have no doubt about it. I know where he has gone.
10 The notices were not sent out till yesterday. I apologize.
11 All the men were heavy smokers. The disease was clearly related to that.
12 Where can you find the money? Don't worry about that.

Exercise 81

Transform each of the pairs of sentences in Exercise 80 so as to form one sentence beginning with a *wh*-clause on the model:

What I am not certain about is who gave him the money.

Postposed prepositions

Exercise 82

Transform each of the sentences below into (a) a *wh*-question, and (b) a sentence with a relative clause, on the following model:

I put the parcel on the top shelf.
a Which shelf did you put the parcel on?
b The shelf I put the parcel on was the top one.

1 I gave your letter to the very handsome-looking man.
2 I haven't dealt with the seventh question yet.
3 I am more accustomed to the American style of spelling.
4 I am most anxious about the front tooth.
5 I am familiar with the shorter dictionary.
6 I am best qualified for the intermediate course.
7 I operated on the wrong patient.
8 I was concerned with later editions of this book.
9 I am not clear about the last word in that sentence.
10 I can least rely on the weakest link in the chain.

Exercise 83

Rewrite the following sentences, putting the verb phrase underlined in the passive:

1 Have you accounted for all the breakages?
2 You have not yet acted on my instructions.
3 We have argued about this question for too long.
4 You should have dealt with the lady's complaint at once.
5 They have not yet entered into serious negotiations.
6 No one has ever looked after this house properly.
7 I don't like people staring at me like that.
8 If you stand there, soldiers are likely to shoot at you.
9 People are talking about her all over the town.
10 But he is not the candidate who we voted for.

Prepositional adverbs

Exercise 84

In the sentences below, replace each prepositional phrase by a prepositional adverb if one is available. If one is not available, put a dash:

1 Drive past the house.
2 Walk to the door.
3 Step into the office.
4 Stand at the back.
5 Go towards Girton.
6 Stay off the road.
7 Get inside the car.
8 Jump onto the bus.
9 We're leaving for Rome.
10 Swim across the river.
11 Climb over the wall.
12 We come from Italy.
13 Wait outside my room.
14 Stroll by her window.
15 He rushed through the town.
16 I am going with Jack.
17 You were in front of me.
18 My room is opposite yours.
19 Don't get out of bed.
20 We have come to the end.

Functions of the prepositional phrase

Exercise 85

Identify each prepositional phrase in the sentences below, and indicate by *a, b, c* or *d* whether it is

a an adverbial (whether adjunct, disjunct or conjunct)
b a postmodifier in a noun phrase
c the complementation of a verb
d the complementation of an adjective.

1 I met John Wilkins when I was at the bank.
2 Then I had lunch with him at a restaurant.
3 In the afternoon, we went to Boston together.
4 We went to see whether John Taylor was at home.
5 I spent five years at a medical school.
6 The students at the hospital were fond of practical jokes.
7 People in pain do not try to hide anything from their doctor.
8 I regret to say that I fainted at my first operation.
9 As a result, I decided to give up medicine.
10 The professor was, in fact, afraid of us.
11 In all fairness, I should add that he suffered from violent pains in the head.
12 In any case, as he had taken his first degree in 1927, he must have been over the retirement age.

Prepositions indicating position and direction

Exercise 86

Say which of the following prepositions

to	at	(away) from
on(to)	on	off
in(to)	in	out of

could acceptably replace each dash in the sentences below:

1 Come $_a$______ my room and sit down $_b$______ my desk.
2 Stand $_a$______ the door and show the visitors $_b$______ their seats.
3 Take this parcel $_a$______ my house. I live $_b$______ 32, Sidgwick Avenue.
4 Stick this notice $_a$______ the notice-board. Don't let anyone take it $_b$______ the notice-board, will you?
5 I don't want anyone else $_a$______ the platform, so please keep right $_b$______ it.
6 Take that dangerous weapon $_a$______ him and keep it $_b$______ him.
7 How far is it $_a$______ here $_b$______ the station?
8 Mary stood $_a$______ the window watching as the dog chased the intruder $_b$______ the garden.
9 Many people work $_a$______ the town and go $_b$______ the country for the week-end.
10 Most government offices are situated $_a$______ the capital, but some have moved $_b$______ the provinces.
11 Do you really live $_a$______ New Delhi? I stopped $_b$______ New Delhi once on the flight $_c$______ Tokyo $_d$______ London.
12 My younger brother is still $_a$______ school. He will be going $_b$______ university next year.

Exercise 87

Replace each dash by one of the following prepositions:
above after before behind below beneath in front of on top of over under underneath

1 If X is above Y, then Y is ______ X.
2 When A is behind B, then B is ______ A.
3 S is under T: so T must be ______ S.
4 U is below V. Therefore V is ______ U.
5 A bridge goes ______ a river, and the river ______ the bridge.
6 *Gamma* comes before *delta,* so *delta* must come ______ *gamma.*
7 We can't move forwards or backwards. There is a bus ______ us and a truck right in our way.
8 The wall collapsed ______ a crowd of people and they were buried ______ the rubble.
9 A swimmer without breathing apparatus must keep his head ______ the surface of the water; but a diver with an aqualung can stay ______ the surface for a long time.
10 We live ______ the hill ______ the town and have a magnificent view ______ the surrounding countryside.

Exercise 88

Replace each dash by one of the following:
across along past through

1 The dog chased the kitten a______ the lawn and b______ the shrubbery.
2 As we were not allowed to go a______ the frontier at X, we drove b______ it as far as Y and crossed it there.
3 The bandit ran a______ the street, fired, and a shot went right b______ the wall behind me.
4 On the Trans-Siberian railway, you travel a______ the shores of Lake Baikal, b______ dark forests, c______ wide plains, d______ herds of grazing cattle.
5 It takes only a few hours to fly a______ the Atlantic. It seems to take almost as long sometimes to drive b______ the dense traffic of a modern urban conglomeration.

Exercise 89

State, by writing *a, b, c, d* etc., whether the preposition underlined indicates

a *position*
b *destination*
c *passage*
d *orientation*
e *resultative state*
f *pervasive (static) state*
g *pervasive motion*

1 The monkeys disappeared through the window.
2 I went into the bathroom to get a drink of water.
3 I looked in the mirror and thought I had a monkey's face.
4 A monkey was sitting on the edge of the bath.
5 It was squeezing toothpaste all over its chest.
6 I rushed out of the house, shouting for help.
7 Out of the house, I felt calmer.
8 I sent for the monkey-catcher, who lived across the river.
9 We ran behind the house and watched.
10 Two monkeys were chasing each other in the dining-room.
11 They were still dancing around the house.
12 I shouted, and one dived under the bed.
13 Paper lay scattered all over the floor.
14 At last they all trooped off down the road.
15 Down the road was an old temple.
16 My best friend lived down the road.
17 His is the white house just past the bridge.
18 If you can get past his dog, you'll be perfectly safe.
19 Come onto the verandah and sit down.
20 Thank goodness, we're over the worst of it now.

Position and direction metaphorically

Exercise 90

Replace each dash by one of the following prepositions used in a metaphorical sense:

above below beneath beyond from in into out of over past to under

1 If you run a_____ difficulties or find yourself b_____ any trouble at all, I'll help you out.
2 We're a_____ no danger now. I can assure you that we're safely b_____ danger at last.
3 I'm sorry, we have no typewriter ribbons a_____ stock. We've been b_____ stock for several days.
4 His attitude in writing this letter is a_____ contempt. It is b_____ my dignity to reply.
5 I'm afraid you're too old. You're a_____ age. I was b_____ the impression you were younger.
6 Don't panic. The situation is a_____ control. The captain knows exactly what to do b_____ the circumstances.
7 You usually find me a_____ a good humour, but, really, your behaviour today is b_____ a joke.
8 You must face facts. You are a_____ your prime, and the time has come when we should release you b_____ your heavy responsibilities.
9 John's work is very good. It is well a_____ the average. But Jack's is b_____ the standard I expect in this class.
10 The purpose of welfare services is to provide security a_____ the cradle b_____ the grave.
11 Owing to circumstances a_____ our control, we have run b_____ debt. The situation is, however, not c_____ hope, and I am confident that we can soon put our affairs d_____ order again.

Prepositions relating to time

Exercise 91

Replace each dash by one of the following prepositions relating to time:

at on in; for during after before; since until by up to

1 The museum is closed a_____ Mondays. Otherwise, it opens every day of the week b_____ 09.00 hours, and remains open to the public c_____ 17.00. All visitors must be out of the building d_____ 17.05.
2 a_____ the summer months, the reading-room will only be open b_____ the mornings, c_____ four hours, namely d_____ 8 a.m. e_____ 12.
3 A How long have these regulations been in force?
B a_____ about six months, b_____ last January.

4 Jackson was born a______ New Year's Day, b______ the morning of January 1st 1912.
5 You will wait here a______ 20.00 hours. You cannot leave b______ then, as the moon will not be out. c______ 20.00, proceed quietly to point X. Wait there for 'C' Company. If 'C' Company has not joined you d______ 21.30, make your own way to point Y. You will not stay at Y e______ 21.30.
6 a______ two hours, we waited at Z for further instructions. At last, a signal came, shortly b______ dawn.

Exercise 92
Supply *on, in* or *zero* (*0*) in place of each of the dashes below. If *on* or *in* is optional, indicate by brackets, thus: (*on*)

1 A meeting was held a______ last Thursday. An account of it appeared in the press b______ Friday last.
2 We shall meet a______ next Thursday, and then again b______ March 20th.
3 A telegram came a______ this morning to say that Roberts is due to arrive b______ Monday next.
4 A a______ the next time you come to London, let me know.
B I come to London b______ every June.
5 A When shall I see you again?
B Perhaps a______ Tuesday week, or b______ the following day.

Exercise 93
If *for* is optional in the following sentences, put (*for*); otherwise *for*:

1 We waited for two hours in the pouring rain.
2 I shall be here for another six weeks.
3 This noise has gone on for too long.
4 I haven't been able to eat anything for two days.
5 For two days, I haven't eaten anything.
6 I have worked in this department for ten years and now I would like a change.
7 No other post will fall vacant for a year or two yet.
8 I think you had better lie down for an hour or two.
9 We have been waiting here for an hour and a half.
10 For two days, the storm raged; and we clung to the wreckage of a ship for two long days and nights.

Prepositions indicating cause and purpose
Exercise 94
Replace each subordinate clause underlined by a prepositional phrase, retaining the original meaning. Do not use the same preposition twice.

1 We were obliged to rest, because it was intensely hot.
2 We were obliged to wear thick, high boots, because we were afraid of poisonous snakes.
3 Because he knew this mountainous country, Jackson was appointed as our guide.
4 I think the chief let us go simply because he sympathized with us in our plight.
5 Many of the prisoners died on the march either because they were starving or because they had been severely wounded.
6 There are criminals who will commit murder because they want money.

Means; instrument; manner; support, opposition; etc.

Exercise 95

Replace each dash by one of the prepositions indicated.

As, like

1 Robert was ______ a brother to me.
2 In calling him my 'friend', I am using that word as I would have used it ______ a child.
3 He was wearing a sports shirt and sandals, ______ a tourist.
4 ______ a boy, he had been very fond of swimming.
5 Be your age. You're behaving ______ a boy.
6 I can offer you a temporary job ______ a clerk.
7 Many people believe they are not ______ other men.
8 ______ a friend, he was always ready to help me.

By, with, without

9 I was always happy to be ______ my friends, enjoying their company.
10 You are a good friend. What would I do ______ you?
11 I must stay here. You go ahead ______ me.
12 I woke ______ a start. Someone was moving downstairs.
13 Thousands of people are away from work ______ influenza.
14 Influenza viruses are studied ______ growing them in fertile hens' eggs.
15 You cannot make a good omelette ______ dried eggs.
16 Nor can you make an omelette ______ breaking eggs.
17 You break the egg ______ tapping it smartly on the edge of the frying-pan.
18 Lift the omelette out of the frying-pan a______ a broad knife, or b______ means of a spatula.

At, by, with

19 We were surprised ______ a loud knock at the door.
20 What a thing to say! I'm surprised ______ you!
21 See if you can keep the children amused ______ this toy.
22 Queen Victoria was not amused ______ naughty stories.
23 I'm amused ______ your reaction to that last example.

24 Rosemary is delighted ______ the flowers you sent her.
25 We are all delighted ______ the news of your engagement.
26 Everyone was shocked ______ hearing of your bereavement.

For, with, against

27 Every vote $_a$______ me will be a vote $_b$______ the party I oppose.
28 We are on your side. We are all ______ you.
29 A skilful politician succeeds in going along ______ public opinion.
30 It is always difficult to stand up ______ the opinion of the majority.
31 If you are $_a$______ the proposal, write 'Yes'. If you are $_b$______ it, write 'No'.

In, with

32 We have studied your proposal $_a$______ great care, but cannot see $_b$______ what way it differs from ours.
33 All the people received the news of the treaty $_a$______ relief, and returned to their homes $_b$______ a glad heart. Those who had fought so valiantly were rewarded $_c$______ a fashion appropriate for heroes.

Of, with, without

34 A man $_a$______ a loaded gun but $_b$______ skill in holding it properly can be a menace.
35 Herbert was a man $_a$______ few words; but he was a man $_b$______ a sense of when to say the right thing.
36 I would rather have a house $_a$______ character than a luxury flat $_b$______ any aesthetic appeal whatever.

Prepositional phrase as disjunct or as conjunct

Exercise 96

Replace the finite clause underlined by a prepositional phrase beginning with one of the following:

despite *or* in spite of   for all   notwithstanding   with all

1 Although the city has so many attractions, Laurie still preferred his cottage in the country.
2 There was clear scientific evidence, but people still refused to believe that cigarette smoking was dangerous.
3 (Article 6 makes provision for compensating a tenant if any defect in the central heating installation results in damage to the tenant's property.) Although this provision is made in Article 6, the landlord will not be responsible for any damage caused by negligence on the part of the tenant.
4 He died a most unhappy man, although he had an immense fortune.
5 You've got a huge secretarial staff yet it still seems to take you a week to answer a simple letter.

Exception

Exercise 97

Indicate, by *a, b, c,* etc., which of the following could **not** replace the dash in the sentences below:

a apart from b but c but for d except e excepting
f except for g with the exception of

1 There will be rain everywhere ______ in the north-east.
2 ______ Harvey, every student failed the test.
3 ______ Harvey, we should never have found the way.
4 Every picture has been sold ______ these two.
5 Every picture ______ these two has been sold.
6 ______ these two, every picture has been sold.
7 We would have arrived two hours ago ______ the traffic jams.

7 The simple sentence

Clause types

Exercise 98

Indicate, by *a, b, c,* etc., to which of the following clause types the sentences below belong:

a	S	V intens.	Cs	
b	S	V intens.	A place	
c	S	V intrans.		
d	S	V monotrans.	Od	
e	S	V complex trans.	Od	Co
f	S	V complex trans.	Od	A place
g	S	V ditrans.	Oi	Od

1 George's father greeted the headmaster.
2 The headmaster put George into the second class.
3 That made Stanley angry.
4 His annoyance did not last.
5 He was really a lawyer.
6 But he proved himself a great soldier.
7 The manager is not in.
8 May I offer you a cup of coffee?
9 After the war, M. gave him back his saddle-bags.
10 He threw himself from his horse.
11 I remember the reasonableness of my father's argument.
12 The parson's cat is an abominable animal.
13 We are in a bit of a mess.
14 I have always lived in the country.
15 Could you call me a porter, please?
16 Do you call yourself a porter?
17 Finding peace and quiet has become very difficult.
18 Every increase in knowledge augments our capacity for evil.
19 The police laid the bodies by the side of the road.
20 Travel nowadays is fraught with disillusion.
21 You must keep calm.

22 Keep out of sight.
23 You can keep the change.
24 Keep your hands off me!
25 I can't keep my hands warm.
26 Keep me a seat, will you?

Exercise 99
Say whether the items underlined in the following sentences are grammatically *obligatory* or *optional*:

1 George's father greeted the headmaster warmly.
2 He greeted us warmly.
3 That made me very annoyed.
4 It made me thoroughly annoyed.
5 George's work was always thorough.
6 Let me give you a drink.
7 Let me explain the difficulty.
8 The burglar stood the ladder against the wall.
9 I don't enjoy loud music.
10 You are being rather stupid.
11 I get impatient with stupid people.
12 He convinced us of his innocence.
13 I always regarded him as innocent.
14 A difficult problem arises in this sentence.
15 Airmen fly aeroplanes.
16 The old lady grew bitter.
17 The luggage weighed twenty kilos.
18 May I suggest a different approach?
19 Please answer this letter by return of post.
20 It gets dark earlier in winter.

Clause types transformed
Exercise 100
Indicate, by *a, b, c,* etc., of which clause types listed in Exercise 98 the following sentences are transformations:

1 People are killed on the roads every day.
2 We were each handed a leaflet.
3 The walls were painted bright pink.
4 He has often been looked upon as slightly mad.
5 All my cards have been laid on the table.
6 Has all this food been paid for?
7 The prisoner was found guilty.
8 His children were found a suitable school.

9 This house has been lived in for two hundred years.
10 Surely I cannot be refused a proper hearing?

SVOO→SVOA

Exercise 101

Supply a prepositional phrase which could replace the indirect object in each of the following sentences:

1 May I ask you a great favour?
2 Listen! I'm going to play you a new record.
3 Can I play you a game of chess?
4 I can change you a cheque if you like.
5 Will you choose me an interesting book?
6 We wish all our friends a very happy New Year.
7 I have left you some soup on the stove.
8 An uncle of mine left me a thousand pounds.
9 Would you throw me that rubber, please?
10 Would you mind bringing me a towel?

Clause elements semantically considered

Exercise 102

Indicate, by *a, b, c,* etc., whether the element underlined is

a S agentive
b S agent./instrumental
c S affected
d S recipient
e O affected
f O recipient
g C current
h C resulting

1 It feels cold today.
2 The cold affects me badly.
3 The cold killed the trees.
4 It is turning quite cold.
5 The bell rang loudly.
6 I heard it ring, too.
7 You've got brains.
8 Use your brains.
9 She lay in his arms.
10 We found the house empty.
11 They left the house empty.
12 I don't like toast burnt.
13 I had those books burnt.
14 Who owns this hat?
15 The table is shaking.
16 Who is shaking it?
17 We laid him on the sofa.
18 We made him some tea.
19 These shoes cut my feet.
20 I'll give you the answer.

Exercise 103

Rephrase the sentences so that O affected becomes S affected:

1 Terrorists blew up the dam.
2 I've broken my glasses.
3 The frost has killed my roses.
4 Someone has moved that picture.
5 A visitor rang the bell.
6 We rolled the car down the hill.
7 The doctor set my broken arm easily.
8 The guard shut the gate quickly.
9 The driver stopped the train.
10 I can't turn this screw.

Exercise 104

Indicate, by *a, b* or *c,* whether the object underlined is

a affected   b effected   c locative

1 Has anyone touched the television today?
2 Who is making all that noise?
3 We are just passing the Eiffel Tower.
4 Take a deep breath.
5 Somebody took my coat by mistake.
6 I climbed the hill as light fell short.
7 A gas leak can cause a serious explosion.
8 We have fought a good fight – and lost.
9 Have you dropped your handkerchief, my dear?
10 After that I paid her a visit every evening.

Subject-verb concord

Exercise 105

Choose an acceptable verb, giving two answers if necessary:

1 Everyone of us {has / have} his own burden to shoulder.
2 It is on each individual effort that the safety and happiness of the whole {depends / depend}
3 What are often regarded as poisonous fungi {is / are} sometimes safely edible.
4 What are these things doing here {is / are} what I'd like to know.
5 War and peace {is / are} a constant theme in history.
6 War and peace {is / are} alternatives between which man must constantly choose.
7 *'War and Peace'* {is / are} a fascinating novel.
8 The people outside {is / are} getting very impatient.
9 The public {is / are} demanding an official enquiry.
10 The Seven Sisters {is / are} a line of chalk cliffs on the coast of Sussex.
11 The seven wonders of the world {was / were} well-known in ancient times.

12 '*The Three Bears*' {is / are} a well-known nursery story.

13 The Philippines {is / are} a large group of islands.

14 None but the brave {deserve / deserves} the fair.

15 Neither John nor Mary {has / have} replied to my letter.

16 I wrote both to John and to Mary. Neither {has / have} replied.

17 Physics, as well as chemistry, {is / are} taught at this school.

18 The employment of girls under sixteen {is / are} forbidden.

19 Everybody {know / knows} what they have to do.

20 How is it that your answer and your neighbour's {is / are} identical?

Other types of concord

Exercise 106

Select an appropriate alternative, noting that more than one may be acceptable.

1 The Committee will insist on {its / their} rights.

2 The Committee wishes to reconsider {its / their} decision.

3 Every passenger has to carry {his / their} own luggage.

4 Wait till everyone has finished before you start taking away {his / their} plates.

5 You have always been such {a good friend / good friends}.

6 George asked Mary if {he / she} would mind choosing some flowers for {his / her} wife.

7 Mary told George that {he / she} had to wait for {his / her} cousin.

8 I consider them {the guilty party / scoundrels}.

9 We have received your estimate for the alterations you propose but have decided that {it / they} would be {too high / unnecessary}.

Negation

Exercise 107

Negate the finite verb in each of the following sentences and make other changes that then become necessary:

1 We have enough evidence already.
2 There is someone doing research in this field.
3 Smoking has something to do with cancer of the lung.
4 Tar from cigarette tobacco, painted onto the skin of mice, produced skin cancer on some of them.
5 This applies to some of the people here already.
6 This experiment has revealed something of importance.
7 It helps us in our daily work, to a certain extent, too.
8 We must go a long way to find someone as good as this.
9 Robertson is still living at this address.
10 He has been away from home a very long time.
11 Hundreds of students can find somewhere comfortable to live.
12 The doctor has sometimes given me some useful advice.
13 There are a lot of people in the auditorium already.
14 I can understand both of these two sentences.
15 I can understand all of these ten words.

Exercise 108

Note the following model:

A There are some people in the auditorium already.
B Oh, I'd say there are very few.
C I agree. There are very few people in the auditorium.

Then, from each of the statements below made by A, produce a suitable comment by C, on the lines of the model above, agreeing with B's rejoinder:

1 A Smoking has something to do with cancer.
  B Ferguson denies that.
2 A We must always go a long way to find someone interested.
  B Oh, I would say seldom.
3 A The experiment has revealed something of importance.
  B Hm, scarcely.
4 A We have all had some experience of real hunger.
  B Surely only two of us have.
5 A I am in favour of making some concessions to the other side.
  B Well, I am against it.
6 A I always see something good on television.
  B You're fortunate. I rarely do.
7 A People have sometimes given an honest answer to that question.
  B I say that few people have.

8 A I remembered to bring some food with me.
B Oh, I forgot to.
9 A There is surely hope of finding some of the passengers alive.
B I am afraid there is very little hope.
10 A There is certain opposition to our proposal.
B I am unaware of it myself.

Exercise 109
Rephrase each of the following sentences, beginning it with the words underlined:

1 We have never heard a more distinguished performance.
2 We seldom receive such generous praise.
3 This nation scarcely ever in the past faced so great a danger.
4 We were never before asked to make a sacrifice of this magnitude.
5 There is rarely an opportunity for us to serve the community in this way.
6 We shall only then begin to realize the appalling danger before us.

Exercise 110
Negate each of the following sentences in two ways, explaining what difference there is, if any, between one way and the other:

1 Many people attended the meeting.
2 All the people were at work.
3 Everyone here agrees with you.
4 Much of the food was bad.
5 One of the runners heard the starting pistol.
6 Another reason for the delay was given.
7 A little of the money was spent on this project.
8 A few of you will have noticed the warning.
9 Half of the work has already been completed.
10 The least of our problems has been solved.

Exercise 111
The sentences below can be interpreted in two ways, according to the scope or focus of negation. Reword them in two ways, so as to make the different meanings clear:

1 I don't lend my books to any of the students.
2 Everything that glitters is not gold.
3 We haven't completed half the work.
4 My instructions do not apply to a few of you.
5 All the people were not informed of the army's plans.
6 We did not inform you because we doubted your loyalty.

7 The meeting was not held on account of your absence.
8 You have not been dismissed in accordance with Clause 6 of your contract.
9 We did not receive your letter because of delays in the post.
10 The patient did not die as a result of your assistance, doctor.

Exercise 112

Note that *I may not go* can have two different meanings illustrated as follows:

	Auxiliary	*Main Verb*
1	I am not allowed to	go
2	I probably will	not go

In 1, the auxiliary is negated; in 2 the main verb is negated. Analyse each of the following unambiguous sentences in one of those ways, and paraphrase each sentence so as to make its meaning quite clear.

1 Susan can't type very fast.
2 She can't use my typewriter tomorrow.
3 They can't be far away now.
4 I may not be very late.
5 They can't have arrived yet.
6 You oughtn't to behave like that.
7 You needn't be alarmed.
8 They won't be very pleased.
9 He won't listen to a word I say.
10 You mustn't leave your coat there.

Questions

Exercise 113

Indicate whether the following questions have positive or negative orientation, and paraphrase them so as to make the orientation clear.

1 Are there some letters for me?
2 Is there any reason for staying here longer?
3 Do you have something to tell me?
4 Have you anything to say in your defence?
5 Will you have some sugar in your coffee?
6 Is there somewhere where we can talk quietly?
7 Will you have any more to eat?
8 Haven't we dealt with this question already?
9 Haven't you finished your essay yet?

Tag questions

Exercise 114

Indicate, by *a, b, c* or *d,* whether the tag questions below can be classified as:

a positive assumption + neutral expectation
b negative ,, + ,, ,,
c positive ,, + positive ,,
d negative ,, + negative ,,

1 I signed the cheque, didn't I?

2 I put in the date, didn't I?

3 I didn't forget, did I?

4 It's all right now, isn't it?

5 It's terrible weather, isn't it?

6 It was worse yesterday, wasn't it?

7 You can all understand, can you?

8 You haven't eaten a thing, have you?

9 John's grown a lot lately, hasn't he?

10 There's a meeting this evening, isn't there?

11 We must go to it, mustn't we?

12 We mustn't be late, must we?

13 You couldn't lend me any money, could you?

14 Woolley's sell watches, don't they?

15 And your father wouldn't buy you one, would he?

16 You slipped a watch into your pocket, didn't you?

17 The shop assistant wouldn't believe you, would he?

18 You don't expect me to believe that, do you?

19 You shouldn't have said that, should you?

20 That's all for now, is it?

Questions with modals

Exercise 115

Say whether reference is being made to *a* the speaker's authority or *b* the listener's:

1 Shall I start?
2 They shall not pass.
3 May I borrow your typewriter?
4 Might I have a look at your paper?
5 You must let me have it back.
6 Can we stay and watch the show?
7 Yes, you can if you want to.
8 Will you wait a minute please?
9 Do I *have* to wait?
10 I shan't keep you long.

Wh-questions

Exercise 116

Form questions to which the word or words underlined would be exact answers:

1 To see Inca architecture at its most impressive, one must go to Macchu Picchu.
2 Europeans knew nothing about this ancient city before 1911.
3 It was rediscovered in 1911.
4 An American, Hiram Bingham, discovered it.
5 His name was Bingham.
6 He was an American.
7 The city had been buried for hundreds of years.
8 It was protected by a canyon 2,000 feet deep.
9 Its temples had been built from huge granite stones.
10 The stones were fitted together without mortar.
11 The world Somerset Maugham entered when, at the age of eighteen, he became a medical student, was a strange one.
12 Somerset Maugham became a medical student at the age of eighteen.
13 It was a world that knew nothing about planes.
14 It also knew nothing about radio.
15 He paid eighteen shillings a week for two rooms.
16 He paid eighteen shillings for two rooms.
17 He paid eighteen shillings for two rooms.
18 He was an unsatisfactory medical student for his heart was not in it.
19 His first novel was called Liza of Lambeth.
20 The producer thought Somerset Maugham's play might just run for the six weeks till the play he had in mind to follow it with could be produced.

Various types of question

Exercise 117

Give two examples of each of the following:

a a *yes–no* question with positive orientation
b ,, ,, ,, ,, negative ,,
c ,, declarative question
d ,, *Wh*-question ending with a preposition
e an alternative question
f ,, exclamatory ,,
g a rhetorical ,,

Commands

Exercise 118

Name the subject, if any, in each of the following sentences:

1 Waiter, bring me the menu please.
2 You read me the next sentence, John.
3 All the men over twenty-one please stand up.
4 Somebody fetch a doctor quickly.
5 Don't move the patient yet.
6 Oh, do be careful of my broken leg.
7 John, you go and look out for the ambulance.
8 George, take the other end of the stretcher.
9 Let each man decide for himself.
10 Don't let anyone shirk his responsibility.

Miscellaneous categories

Exercise 119

Paraphrase each of the following stretches of language so as to make its meaning quite clear.

1 What beautiful weather we're having!
2 How I have waited for this moment!
3 What about having some dinner with me?
4 Far be it from me to tempt you against your will.
5 In for a penny, in for a pound.
6 Waste not, want not.
7 Now for the crucial question!
8 The sooner the better.
9 What to see in Paris.
10 Road works ahead.

Newspaper headlines

Exercise 120

Identify the elements of clause structure (by S, V, Od, Oi, Cs, Co, A) in the headlines below. Then expand each headline into a sentence such as would occur in the report beneath the headline in a newspaper.

1 HOLIDAYS PRICE WAR STARTS
2 HUGHES TAKES SUNDERLAND INTO SIXTH ROUND
3 DRIVER ENTERED FOG AT 100 m.p.h.
4 FARMER IN VAN RAMS SUSPECT PLANE
5 IMMIGRATION RULES CRITICIZED
6 OIL POLLUTION MEASURES TO BE TESTED
7 EXTRA PARKS FOR VEHICLES
8 MOON DUST VANISHES
9 AIRPORT NOISE DROVE HUSBAND MAD
10 SCOTLAND CHAMPIONS AGAIN

8 Adjuncts, disjuncts, conjuncts

Exercise 121

Using only information contained in the passage below, compose sentences so that each one contains an adverbial, and each adverbial is realized by a different one of the following units:

1 an adverb phrase
2 a noun phrase
3 a prepositional phrase
4 a finite clause
5 an infinitive clause
6 an *-ing* participle clause
7 an *-ed* participle clause
8 a verbless clause

'Forster arrived at Nassenheide one morning in April. He was early, but went straight to the castle. When Herr Steinweg opened the door, Forster explained that he had come to take up his duties as tutor. Herr Steinweg wished to appear friendly, and welcomed Forster in. Forster felt relieved, though he was not aware that his host was rather annoyed at his unexpected arrival.'

Criteria for distinguishing adjuncts from disjuncts and conjuncts

Exercise 122

Indicate by *a* if, in the sentence concerned, the adverbial in brackets can occur initially, and by *b* if it can occur initially as an adjunct.

1 Forster knocked at the door. (Nervously)
2 He did not know their names. (Naturally)
3 He got on well with his hosts. (In no time)
4 He found his host's daughter very shy. (However)
5 Ilsa could not speak English. (Fluently)
6 He could not talk with her. (Frankly)
7 He came to like her. (Gradually)
8 She was not accustomed to meeting young men. (Obviously)
9 He did not make her work. (Very hard)
10 She did not make much progress. (As a result)

Exercise 123

From the following list, select suitable adjuncts which could be the focus of a question or of clause negation in the sentences below:

absolutely	fluently	in the drawing-room	publicly
actually	frankly	in the morning	quickly
at once	gradually	in the evening	rightly
coolly	haltingly	late	warmly
early	hard	nearly	well
evasively	hardly	nervously	with difficulty
eventually	in any case	of course	without strain

1 Did Forster arrive at Nassenheide a______ or b______?
2 He arrived a______, and not b______ when he was expected.
3 Did Herr Steinweg receive him a______ or b______?
4 Did Ilsa speak English a______ or did she speak it b______?
5 Did Forster come to like her a______, or was it b______?
6 He did not make her work a______, but allowed her to work b______.
7 Did she make progress a______, or did progress come b______?
8 She was not accustomed to meeting young men a______, but she sometimes met them b______.
9 He could not talk with her a______, but had to express himself b______.
10 Did Forster get on a______ with his hosts, or did relations with them develop b______.

Syntactic features of adverbials
Exercise 124

a In the first three of the sentences below, use a pro-form in the second clause which will echo the adjunct of the first clause:

1 Herr Steinweg speaks English fluently, and his son speaks English fluently too.
2 Forster began the conversation nervously, and Ilsa began the conversation nervously, too.
3 I can do this easily, and you can do it easily too.

b In the next three sentences, use an adjunct as the focus of *only*:

4 Forster only came to like her ______.
5 He only worked seriously ______.
6 She could only speak English ______.

c In the next three, use an adjunct as the focus of *also*:

7 He only came to like her gradually; but he also came to admire her ______.
8 He only worked intensively in the morning; but he also worked a little ______.
9 She could only speak English haltingly; but she also spoke it very ______.

d Convert the next three into cleft sentences with focus on the adjunct underlined:

10 He arrived at Nassenheide <u>in April.</u>
11 He came to understand the local customs <u>with difficulty.</u>
12 She only met young men in the <u>drawing-room.</u>

Exercise 125
Supply a different adjunct to fill each of the gaps, and explain the function of the adjunct so supplied in the sentence concerned:

1 Herr Steinweg's son spoke more ______ than Ilsa did.
2 However ______ she spoke, her diction was always very clear.
3 How ______ did Herr Steinweg receive his guest?
4 How ______ she looked at him!
5 So ______ did she speak that Forster was obliged to exercise great patience when listening to her.

Classification of adjuncts
Exercise 126
Identify the adjuncts in the sentences below, and state (a) *the class,* and (b) *the subclass,* if any, to which each adjunct could be allotted:

1 Prince Albert foresaw great changes in the framework of society.
2 The masses now hold strong views.
3 I heard a machine which haltingly reproduced the human voice.
4 We even thought it was going to explode.
5 No one can really be informed about all these questions.
6 I simply did not have the technical knowledge required.
7 Something happens to make the answer completely wrong.
8 Suddenly, the door swung open.
9 The train stopped suddenly.
10 A man's real influence is only exerted after his death.
11 Butler was conceited and rather self-conscious.
12 An unstable community is especially liable to suspect its neighbours.
13 Artistically, the work had little merit.
14 Lytton Strachey ranked much of Hugo's poetry highly.
15 He was highly critical of one particular play of Hugo's.
16 Hugo's revolutionary aims were purely literary.
17 His call for an overthrow of the old classical drama rang out far beyond the literary world.
18 Conservatives heard the call with alarm.
19 A queue of long-haired, strangely dressed youths formed outside the theatre.
20 You see three-quarters of his figure, to just above the knees.
21 He is standing almost square.

22 When you start looking especially at his body, you move naturally from the top.
23 The eyes are a little sad if you look at them alone.
24 His right hand, entirely shadowed, is on his hip.
25 This style of conversation is quite different from that of rhetoric.
26 That is one of those fruitful ideas that can carry society forward.
27 These ideas are already improving society.
28 We shall find that the Greeks and Romans, too, overran the world in their day.
29 They deliberately spread their culture.
30 As far as culture is concerned, their influence remains today.

Intensifiers

Exercise 127

Use one of the following intensifiers to fill the gaps below. Do not use the same intensifier twice.

absolutely	deeply	far	keenly
actually	definitely	fully	totally
badly	entirely	greatly	utterly
bitterly	exceedingly	heartily	violently
completely	extremely	highly	well

1 It was really ______ kind of you to help us.
2 I am ______ grateful to you.
3 We all feel ______ more certain of our position now.
4 The clerk's story was ______ exaggerated.
5 Did you ______ hear him threaten the girl?
6 I am sure she must have been ______ shaken.
7 I am ______ amazed to hear you say that.
8 You will ______ regret this one day.
9 We were all ______ moved by his story.
10 The result of the elections is now ______ confirmed.
11 The situation has ______ changed.
12 We are not ______ satisfied with the result.
13 Mr Chairman, I ______ support the last speaker's remarks.
14 We ______ agree with your proposal.
15 Stevens is ______ interested in his work.
16 We need technicians who are ______ trained.
17 All the guests were ______ ill that night.
18 I can ______ imagine how the poor hostess felt.
19 We ______ reject your accusations against us.
20 I can see what you mean. I am not ______ blind.

The positions of adverbials

Exercise 128

Indicate the position of the adverbials in the following sentences by one of these four symbols:

I (=initial) M1 (=medial 1) M2 (=medial 2) F (=final)

1 Honestly, I don't believe a word of it.
2 I honestly don't know what to say.
3 He was never a man to answer one honestly.
4 I still haven't had any reply.
5 I am still waiting for a reply.
6 I quite understand your predicament.
7 He can speak English very well if he wants to.

Exercise 129

Indicate, by the symbol I, M1, M2 or F, which position in the sentence concerned the adverbial in brackets could occupy. Give more than one symbol when that would be appropriate:

1 The terrain was explored (scientifically).
2 The argument was absurd (scientifically).
3 I do not understand you (simply).
4 Perhaps you will understand if I speak (simply).
5 He made me angry (thoroughly).
6 You have studied this chapter (thoroughly).
7 I appreciate your kindness (much).
8 I appreciate it (very much).
9 I mean what I say (honestly).
10 John always writes to me (honestly).
11 If you do not know the details, you may answer the question (generally).
12 These questions are not difficult and we can answer most of them (generally).
13 Your theory may be right. However, you will find it very difficult to apply (practically).
14 Such enormous distances are impossible to imagine (practically).
15 This is my business (hardly).
16 I can hear you (hardly).
17 I can hear you (just).
18 This is for your ears (only).
19 This is for your ears (alone).
20 Will you come this way? (kindly).
21 I thought I spoke to her (kindly).
22 I spoke to her mother (also).
23 I spoke to her mother (as well).
24 The house needs re-painting (badly).

25 They have painted it (badly).
26 It has been painted (badly).
27 We have to live (economically).
28 We have to manage (somehow).
29 We feel disheartened (sometimes).
30 We shall surrender (never).

Only, also

Exercise 130

1 Change the position of *only* in the sentence:
We only discuss financial matters at our sub-committee meeting on Thursdays,

so as to focus attention as follows:

a on 'financial matters'
b on 'our sub-committee meeting'
c on 'on Thursdays'.

2 Replace by a cleft sentence each of the three new sentences so formed.
3 Write out the original sentence three times, stressing the words that would receive nuclear stress in speech in making the three different focuses referred to in (1).
4 Repeat the three operations – (1), (2) and (3) – replacing *only* by *also*.

Exercise 131

Illustrate, by means both of nuclear stress and of cleft sentences, possible differences in meaning between the two members of these pairs of sentences:

1 a Only a man's real influence is exerted after his death.
b A man's real influence is only exerted after his death.
2 a We can only expect to save our own homes by such a strategy.
b We can expect to save our own homes only by such a strategy.
3 a The Government has also made this announcement through the press.
b The Government has made this announcement through the press also.

Position and direction adjuncts

Exercise 132

Say whether the place adjuncts in the sentences below refer to position or direction:

1 We are going to the West Indies.
2 My parents live in the West Indies.
3 The horse jumped over the fence.
4 It was safely over the fence.
5 I must have stepped on some glass.
6 We got into the bus very hurriedly.

7 Wait at the gate till you hear the whistle.
8 They worked for six months in a tunnel.
9 They tunnelled their way into the rock.
10 Inside the tank, the temperature had fallen twenty degrees.
11 The thermometer had slipped inside the tank.
12 The bull charged furiously at the gate.

Exercise 133

Indicate, by *a*, if the phrase underlined is a place adjunct, and by *b* if it is a postmodifier in a noun phrase:

1 The spectators were sitting in the grandstand.
2 The spectators in the grandstand were singing.
3 I take my car to the garage in the village.
4 In the village, there are several old cottages.
5 A house was destroyed near us.
6 The house next to ours was damaged.
7 Oranges in Spain are huge.
8 The olive oil in my country is delicious.
9 Upstairs the people are having a party.
10 The people upstairs are rather noisy.

Exercise 134

If the phrases in the brackets below are place adjuncts, indicate (A) which of the pair would normally come first when both follow the verb, and (B) which could begin the sentence concerned:

1 Everyone goes ([a]in our village, [b]to the supermarket).
2 People like to eat ([a]in Italy, [b]out of doors).
3 You will find a note ([a]in an appendix, [b]at the back).
4 I always keep a dictionary ([a]on the shelf, [b]beside my desk).
5 They rushed ([a]into the sea, [b]down the hill).
6 We live ([a]in the house, [b]across the road).
7 People were running ([a]everywhere, [b]into the streets).
8 You can catch the express train ([a]to Cherbourg, [b]from Paris).
9 I can see ([a]as far as Hampstead, [b]from here).
10 We crept ([a]into our sleeping bags, [b]on the narrow ledge).

***Up* as place adjunct or as intensifier**

Exercise 135

Indicate, by *a*, if *up* is used as a prepositional adverb of direction, or by *b* if it is used perfectively:

1 Come up and see me some time.
2 Can I help you up?

3 I'm saving up for a trip to Tokyo.
4 Drink this up while it's hot.
5 There's no electricity. We must *walk* up.
6 It has gone half past nine. You must wake up.
7 When I grow up, I'll throw all these things away.
8 Let's lock up and go to bed.
9 If you're going to bed now, will you take this glass up with you?
10 My shoelace is undone. I must tie it up.

Time adjuncts
Exercise 136
The phrases in the brackets are time adjuncts. Indicate (A) which of them would normally come first when both follow the verb, and (B) which could begin the sentence concerned:

1 Term will begin ([a]next year, [b]on January 9th).
2 I got home ([a]last night, [b]very late).
3 Where were you ([a]on Friday, [b]at six o'clock)?
4 There was a heavy snowfall ([a]in April, [b]in 1929).
5 There were several heavy snowfalls ([a]during the first four months, [b]that year).
6 I was away ([a]during the summer, [b]for three weeks).
7 I was born ([a]on March 15th, [b]1956).
8 You were not here ([a]in March, [b]in 1956).

Time adjuncts with *for, since* and *till*
Exercise 137
Supply *for, since* or *till*:

1 We have been studying this book ______ the beginning of the year.
2 We have been studying this chapter ______ last week.
3 We have been studying it ______ the last week.
4 We shall go on studying this book ______ the end of the year.
5 Thus we shall have been studying it ______ a whole year.
6 You have been doing better lately ______ you stopped going out at night.
7 My father was at home ill ______ several weeks. He has ______ gone into hospital.
8 ______ when you have been in this class?
9 ______ how long have you been in charge?
10 ______ when do you intend to stay?
11 ______ how long do you propose to be here?
12 I propose to be here ______ another month.

Frequency adjuncts

Exercise 138

Classify the following *frequency adjuncts* under the headings given below:

again	continually	occasionally	repeatedly
always	frequently	often	seldom
as a rule	generally	on three occasions	sometimes
as usual	many times	once	twice
at all times	normally	rarely	usually
constantly	now and again	regularly	weekly

1 DEFINITE FREQUENCY

A Period B Number

2 INDEFINITE FREQUENCY

C Usual D Continuous/Continual

E High frequency F Low or zero frequency

Exercise 139

Replace the words or phrases underlined by frequency adjuncts:

1 I go out very little these days.
2 I listen to records quite a lot.
3 Some students fail examinations.
4 None of our students fail.
5 We don't see very much of you now.
6 Many people come to visit the castle.
7 A few of them ask to see the dungeons.

Frequency adjuncts with negation

Exercise 140

Which of the following frequency adjuncts could **not** normally fill the gaps in the sentences below:

a always	c frequently	e normally	g sometimes
b continually	d generally	f often	h usually

1 He ______ did not finish working until midnight.
2 We ______ don't serve meals after ten o'clock.

Which of the frequency adjuncts listed above *could* fill both the gaps in the following sentence:

3 We ______ don't serve meals after ten o'clock, though ______ we do.

***Already, still, yet* etc.**

Exercise 141

Indicate, by *a, b, c,* etc., whether the gap in each of these sentences can be filled by:

a already b any longer c any more
d by now e no more f still g yet

1 I ______ know the answer to that question.
2 I know the answer to it ______.
3 We have ______ done this once.
4 They have finished ______.
5 We ______ have done it.
6 I ______ had my passport.
7 I had ______ my passport.
8 I had my passport ______.
9 There's plenty of time ______.
10 We have ______ to see what he can do.
11 We haven't finished this ______.
12 You haven't finished it ______, surely?
13 You ______ haven't done it properly.
14 The engine ______ wasn't working.
15 The engine wasn't ______ working.
16 Have you read that article ______?
17 Haven't you read it ______?
18 Do you ______ love me?
19 Don't you ______ like me?
20 Don't you like me ______?
21 Wasn't the train moving ______?
22 Was it ______ moving?
23 Had it stopped ______?
24 Are you ______ not smoking?
25 Aren't you ready ______?
26 I won't need this book ______.
27 I'll trouble you ______.
28 I am sure they have arrived ______.
29 We ______ have to find out the truth.
30 I shall speak about this subject ______.

Relative position of time adjuncts
Exercise 142
Insert the time adjuncts (in brackets) into the sentence concerned, first (a) putting the 'time when' adjunct at the end of the sentence, then (b) putting it at the beginning:

1 I pay my rates (this year, once a month).
2 The telephone rang (while you were out, twice).
3 We have lectures (this week, all the morning, every day).
4 I shall be away (this summer, for a day or two, several times).

5 There were power cuts (during the winter of 1947, almost every day, for two or three hours at a time).
6 Interviews will take place (every week-day, next month, between nine and twelve).
7 Visits to the museum will be (during the summer, between two and four).

Relative position of process, place and time adjuncts

Exercise 143

Comment on the relative position of the adjuncts in the sentences below: saying whether the order is normal or whether it deviates from the norm for a particular reason.

1 The *Daedalus* sailed back to Europe in 1848.
2 The *Daedalus* was in the South Atlantic on a dark and cloudy afternoon in 1848.
3 The captain was waiting quietly on the quarter-deck.
4 Towards evening, the officer on duty pointed excitedly towards the west.
5 A strange object was moving with incredible speed across the water.
6 The *Daedalus* docked at Plymouth on October 4th.
7 I thought you said it docked on October 4th at Bristol.
8 We waited while the ship docked quietly.
9 We waited for several hours where the men were to come ashore.
10 Wives, mothers and sweethearts waited on the quay with highly commendable patience.

Disjuncts

Exercise 144

Classify the disjuncts in the sentences below as
a *style disjuncts* b *attitudinal disjuncts*

1 Honestly, I was nowhere near the scene of the accident when it happened.
2 I was, indeed, several miles away.
3 Luckily, someone managed to get in touch with me.
4 I was off duty, strictly speaking.
5 Confidentially, the driver was inexperienced.
6 As a matter of fact, he had only just passed his driving test.
7 Quite rightly, you telephoned the hospital first.
8 Foolishly, the girl who answered the telephone did not ask your name.
9 I think, personally, that the girl is rather stupid.
10 Her appointment has not yet been confirmed, understandably.

Exercise 145

Transform the sentences below in one of the following three ways:

a Clearly, there has been a mistake
→ It is clear that there has been a mistake.

b Fortunately, Roberts returned the cheque
→ It is fortunate that Roberts should have returned the cheque.

c Rightly, Roberts returned the cheque *or* Rightly, the cheque was returned by Roberts
→ Roberts was right to return the cheque.

1 Luckily, someone managed to find me.
2 You telephoned the hospital first, quite rightly.
3 Foolishly, the girl did not ask your name.
4 Understandably, her appointment has not been confirmed.
5 Curiously, the dog never barked.
6 Wisely, all the doors had been bolted.
7 We shall clearly have to inform the police.
8 Not unnaturally, we had all felt rather alarmed.
9 The incident happened, possibly, when I was in the garden.
10 What is more important, we should not let it happen again.

Conjuncts

Exercise 146

From the following list, supply a suitable conjunct to link the two sentences in each of the pairs below, without using the same conjunct twice:

at the same time	for instance	on the contrary	thereafter
equally	hence	on the one hand	therefore
first	however	on the other hand	
for example	nevertheless	similarly	

1 In the year 1500, Europe knew less about science than Archimedes, who died in 212 B.C. ______ medievalism made an important contribution to the formation of the scientific movement.

2 The habit of exact thought was implanted by scholastic logic. ______, the greatest contribution of medieval scholarship was the belief that every occurrence can be correlated with its antecedents.

3 It is a great mistake to conceive this historical revolt as an appeal to reason. ______, it was a return to the contemplation of brute fact.

4 There are several factors that contribute to wisdom. ______, there is a sense of proportion.

5 Sight and sound and touch are bound up with our own bodies and cannot be made impersonal. Our emotions start ______ from ourselves.

6 It is possible to make a continual approach towards impartiality: ______, by knowing things somewhat remote in time or space; and, ______, by giving to such things their due weight in our feelings.

7 With every increase of knowledge and skill, wisdom becomes more necessary, for every such increase augments our capacity for realizing our purposes, and ______ augments our capacity for evil, if our purposes are unwise.

8 There are distortions in art which seem to many people unnatural, and ______ shocking: ______, those that we see in some of Picasso's work or in the sculpture of Henry Moore.

9 Morality must be realistic and theory must be related to practice. ______ in politics we must make our moral judgments realistic enough to be political judgments.

10 One of the tragic things about intercommunal strife is that both parties quickly believe the worst of each other. And, ______, each of the antagonists insists that its own actions are inspired by lofty ideals.

11 In those countries where the media of mass communication are commercial enterprises, success is generally measured by the size of the audience. People are more likely to buy a newspaper, ______, if their attention is caught by something sensational.

12 Unnumbered years before the Spaniards' coming, the beautiful wife of an Indian Chief, to whom she had been unfaithful, came to this lonely spot and drowned herself in the cold waters of the Guatavita. Every year ______ the unhappy chief came to the lake with offerings of gold.

Exercise 147

Classify the conjuncts on the right side of the vertical line by arranging them in the subclasses listed on the left:

Subclasses	*Conjuncts*	
1 antithetic	above all	after all
2 apposition	alternatively	by the way
3 concessive	consequently	equally
4 enumerative	finally	for example
5 equative	furthermore	hence
6 inferential	in conclusion	in contrast
7 reformulatory	in other words	in the first place
8 reinforcing	in that case	in the meantime
9 replacive	incidentally	meanwhile
10 result	nevertheless	on the contrary
11 summative	on the other hand	otherwise
12 temporal transition	rather	similarly
13 transitional	therefore	to sum up

9 Coordination, apposition and ellipsis

Ellipsis in dependent clauses

Exercise 148

Rewrite the following sentences omitting whatever can be ellipted without change of meaning:

1 When you are in Rome, do as Rome does.
2 When he was pressed to take part in politics, he firmly declined.
3 There were no stores of boots that were readily available.
4 He threw himself from his horse and lay still as if he had been shot.
5 Any foreigner, however innocent he might be, was attacked.
6 If you were left alone on a desert island, what would you do first?
7 If other people are willing to make and use machines for my benefit, I am not less willing to let them make and use machines for my benefit.
8 I do not wish to take part in this protest, and I do not intend to take part in it.
9 Unless you are travelling by the coach, please let the Secretary know when you expect to arrive.
10 The castle, which was built in the twelfth century, has dominated the valley ever since.
11 Much of the earth's surface is formed by sedimentary rocks – that is to say, rocks which were formed by the deposition of sand, silt and clay.
12 Our atmosphere, while it is beneficial for life in general, prevents us from seeing the universe in any but a very restricted range of light.

Exercise 149

Expand the following ellipted sentences so as to make their meaning clearer:

1 See you tomorrow then.
2 See anything interesting?
3 Anybody coming my way?
4 Anybody telephone?
5 Had a good time?
6 Sorry, had to find my coat.
7 Sorry you didn't come with us?
8 Thought you were never coming.
9 Anything else you want?
10 Anything on the news last night?
11 Anything the matter with your foot?
12 Surprised you didn't hurt yourself more seriously.

Coordination and subordination

Exercise 150

If the order of the clauses in the following sentences can be reversed, answer *Yes*; otherwise *No*:

1 The young lady looked at me disdainfully and went on with her telephone conversation.
2 We were sitting in the car outside the house, when the inspector called.
3 We were sitting in the car outside the house, when up the road came a tall, lean man.
4 We went everywhere together, as we were very close friends.
5 We told each other all our secrets, for we were very close friends.
6 He excelled in every walk of life, and yet he always kept a certain backwoods simplicity.
7 As soon as I know, I'll ring you up.
8 Whenever I have a problem, I'll give you a ring.
9 The Director took a great dislike to me, and he did not attempt to hide it.
10 He took a great dislike to me, although he did his best to conceal it.

Exercise 151

Omit the subject only, in any clause other than the first, when such ellipsis would be acceptable:

1 The Director took a dislike to us and he did not attempt to conceal it.
2 He took a dislike to us because he objected to our being together so much.
3 He made life difficult for us, because he guessed we knew of his involvement in the conspiracy and because he thought we would report him.
4 We knew all about the plot, yet we said nothing to our comrades.
5 He was not sure of this, so he kept an eye on us continually.
6 We pretended to whisper to our colleagues, so that we gave him the impression that we were talking about him.
7 One morning, he waited for us, then he asked us to come into his office.
8 We told him we had both been on the premises that evening; however, we did not say that we had seen him there.

Semantic implications of coordination

Exercise 152

Explain the semantic relationship between the two coordinate clauses of each of the following sentences, and make the relationship explicit by adding an adverbial:

1 I often see men who went to school with me and who have done well for themselves.
2 I am a professional man of letters and a typewriter is essential to my work.

3 If other people are willing to make and use machines for my benefit, and they seem willing and eager to do so, I am not less willing to let them do so.
4 These sharks are very dangerous, and they have never attacked me so far.
5 Lay a hand on me and I'll scream.
6 A coral reef is a flower garden of stone, and it is filled with the most colourful varieties of life.
7 Another prospect remains to be considered and that is a combination of bridge and tube or tunnel.
8 Now that our son is able to walk, we lay ladders flat instead of leaving them propped up against things; and we shut the garden gate.
9 Man is the only animal that tortures its own species for amusement; and during much of his evolution he has been busily engaged in ruining his own habitat.
10 Japan's position on the edge of the monsoon region has made highly productive rice cultivation possible, and the Japanese islands are surrounded by rich fishing grounds.

Exercise 153

Explain the semantic relationship between the clauses of each of the following sentences, and make the relationship explicit by adding an adverbial:

1 Let go of me or I'll scream.
2 People envy me for not having a telephone, or they regard me as eccentric.
3 Elizabeth was sound asleep, or at least she pretended to be.
4 This is an early Rembrandt, or it is an excellent forgery.
5 It must be a forgery, or it would be in a museum.
6 Either an animal is protected during the early stages of its learning about the world around it, or the knowledge of which way to respond is built into its nervous system.
7 At noon the sun blazes down with relentless fury, but during the long night the cold is intense.
8 Further research will probably enable us to decide between the two theories, but this is not the same as solving 'the mystery of the creation'.
9 The radio has not banished style from English prose, but it has done much to banish grandiloquence.
10 Mankind has made unprecedented progress during the twentieth century, in many spheres; but something has seriously gone wrong.

Correlatives

Exercise 154

Combine each of the following pairs of simple sentence so as to form one sentence containing EITHER *both . . . and* OR *either . . . or* OR *neither . . . nor* OR *no(t) . . . but* OR *not only . . . but also*:

1 Sometimes my old school friends nod a quick greeting and walk on when they see me. Sometimes they avert their eyes to a shop window.
2 George shouted a friendly greeting to me. Then he came over and shook me warmly by the hand.
3 The fire destroyed St Paul's Cathedral. It also destroyed the Guildhall.
4 The primitive fire engines had no effect on the conflagration. Furthermore, pulling down half-timbered buildings in the path of the fire had no result whatever.
5 In 1666 fire-fighters set up fire-posts with communications between them. The same thing was done in 1940.
6 The city was not abandoned after the fire of 1666. It was not abandoned after the fires of 1940.
7 I have given up using a telephone. What is more, I have given my typewriter away.
8 I have no objection to other people driving cars. I refuse to drive one myself.
9 If a shark comes towards you, you must not show fear. You must not dart away when one comes into view either.
10 Some zoologists thought the strange creature was a rorqual. Other zoologists thought it was a giant squid.

Ellipsis in coordinated clauses
Exercise 155
Rewrite the following sentences omitting whatever can be ellipted without change of meaning:

1 The Chinese are as interested in food as are the French, and the Chinese go to immense trouble to see that it is properly cooked.
2 The Cantonese have developed an astonishing variety in their cooking and they have brought the preparation of sharksfin soup to an exceedingly fine art.
3 Chinese food has to be served in small pieces, it has to be picked up little by little with chopsticks, and it has to be eaten slowly.
4 Rice is generally eaten in the south of the country, but wheat is generally eaten in the north.
5 The meat and vegetables are cut up very small in the kitchen, they are cooked in a large iron bowl, and they are served hot.
6 Fat is used for cooking in northern Europe, but oil is used for cooking in China.
7 Szechuan is the best place for chillies and Canton is the best place for stuffed snails.
8 The Chinese eat their food with chopsticks, the Europeans eat their food with knives and forks.
9 European marriages are often celebrated with champagne, Chinese marriages are often celebrated with a meal of at least a dozen courses..

10 A western-style dinner would not include bread on the menu, nor would a Chinese dinner include rice on the menu.
11 Many people have been suffering from influenza, and many people still are suffering from influenza.
12 You say people have influenza two or three times a year, but they don't really have influenza two or three times a year.
13 During an epidemic many people seem to escape infection but they do not really escape infection.
14 A young animal has to decide which of the things around it are to be eaten and which of the things around it are to be avoided.
15 Some animals swallow highly dangerous objects, others instinctively avoid highly dangerous objects.
16 The young animal is playing a game which can be very dangerous and often is very dangerous.
17 The young animal is protected from danger by its parents, or is protected from danger by some mechanism built into its nervous system from the start.
18 Some people require eight hours' sleep a night, others are satisfied with six hours' sleep a night or less.
19 We cannot give a formula for individual sleep requirements, nor can we give a reliable average of sleep requirements for different age groups.
20 People who pride themselves on needing little sleep may imagine themselves more efficient than others, but in fact they often prove to be less efficient than others.

Ellipsis in noun and prepositional phrases

Exercise 156

Rewrite, omitting whatever can be ellipted without change of meaning:

1 Ellipsis is possible in noun phrases and prepositional phrases.
2 Ellipsis can be used to shorten long sentences and cumbersome sentences.
3 Sentences in legal documents and sentences in students' essays are often too long.
4 For these reasons and other reasons it is worth considering how to make sentences shorter.
5 Your experience and my experience are equally useful.
6 Your experience and your common sense are a great asset to us.
7 He has worked to the full extent of his obligations and beyond his obligations.
8 I do not write to a pre-arranged plot, and have never written to a pre-arranged plot.

Combinatory and segregatory coordination

Exercise 157

Explain the ambiguity in the following sentences:

1 Red, white and blue flags were flying from every balcony.
2 George and Mary are married.
3 George and Mary won a cup.
4 John and Elizabeth did not win anything.
5 George and Mary went home to their parents.

Apposition

Exercise 158

Point out what noun phrases are in apposition to each other in the following sentences; and indicate, by the symbols A to Bc, whether the apposition is
A Restrictive
B Non-restrictive
a equivalent/b attributive/c inclusive

1 Your cousin Robert has just arrived.
2 Robert Ross, your cousin, is on the telephone.
3 The Commander, Captain Peter McKay, was pacing the quarter-deck.
4 Another officer and a midshipman, John Sartoris, were keeping watch from the bridge.
5 Captain McKay was on the quarter-deck, that part of the deck which is reserved for officers.
6 Sartoris was a midshipman, a junior officer in training.
7 All the men swore they saw a sea serpent, a dark-brown monster with a mane like that of a horse.
8 The journal *The Illustrated London News* published an account of the incident.
9 My Lords Commissioners of the Admiralty, the senior officials of the navy, were highly sceptical.
10 An enquiry was held at Plymouth, the port where the ship docked.
11 The court room, an eighteenth century building, was crowded with excited people.
12 The officers, Captain McKay and Sartoris particularly, were questioned closely.
13 The fact that the ship's company had seen this creature aroused tremendous excitement.
14 The truth, that what they had seen was really a wave, began to dawn on them at last.

10 Sentence connection

Sentence connecters

Exercise 159

Comment on all of the devices used for connecting the sentences in the following passages, using the categories and terms listed in the left-hand column:

A. *Lexical*
synonyms
near-synonyms
antonyms
a particular set of items

B. *Syntactic*

1 *Time relaters*
a previous
b simultaneous
c subsequent
d ordinals
e tense
f aspect

2 *Place relaters*

3 *Logical connecters*
a addition
b apposition
c concession
d contrast
e disjunct
f enumeration
g inference
h pro-form
i reformulation
j replacement

1 Many a traveller coming for the first time to Istanbul feels a pang of disappointment. The domes and minarets look well from afar, and there are still fine monuments to be seen. But when we enter the city there is so much that is ugly and commonplace.

2 Thirty-five years ago, George Sampeter and I sat in the same class. We were friends, by which I mean that he was easy with me and I liked him and was easy with him. You will see that I am using 'friends' in the sense in which I would have used it as a child. Now, before I use that word, I must, as it were, look behind my back.

3 An African chief, a man whom I had met in his own country, came to New York when he was well past sixty. He had never before left his own country, and he flew over here, rocketed, as it were, in a matter of hours from his own simple and familiar surroundings to the complex and shifting crowds of a great American city.

4 One afternoon I was sitting on the wall that divided our garden from the churchyard next door. Eight, was I, perhaps, or nine? There is nothing by which I can tell. I contemplated the stones a few feet away and saw that several of them were flat up against our wall. I remember then that I had seen and thought enough.

5 In the year 1619, the bakers of Amsterdam applied to increase the price of bread. They sent in support a complete description of a bakery and its weekly costs.

k result
l substitution
m summation
n transition
o use of *and, but, for*
4 *Structural parallelism*

Thirteen people there were in such an establishment: the baker and his wife, six paid employees, two apprentices, and the baker's three children. Food cost more than anything else, more than raw materials and nearly four times as much as wages. The cost of clothing was included, too, not only for man, wife and children but for the apprentices as well.

6 One bright morning when I was nineteen, I packed all I had on my back, left my native village and walked up to London looking for gold and glory. That was more than fifteen years ago, and I have been here ever since. I shall probably stay here for the rest of my life. Yet in spite of all that, I still cannot think of myself as a Londoner, nor ever will, nor ever want to.

7 The manager of the Theatre Royal put on a play that failed. The next play he had arranged to put on was not ready, and he was at his wits' end. He read a play of mine, called *Lady Frederick*. Though he did not much like it, he thought it might just run for the six weeks till the play he had in mind to follow it with could be produced. It ran for fifteen months. Within a short while I had four plays running at the same time. Nothing of the kind had ever happened before.

8 Many people think that Big Ben is the huge clock that towers 316 feet above the River Thames at Westminster. But, strictly speaking, Ben is the deep-voiced bell which booms from the belfry at the top of 336 steep stairs.

9 With the progress of science, many relationships have been discovered between sunspots and things on earth and in the atmosphere. There are two main reasons for this. First, the scientist has developed new and more sensitive instruments for measuring solar radiations. But undoubtedly the main reason is my second one: over the last forty years we have been studying the upper atmosphere, as distinct from the lower, and all kinds of phenomena have been discovered there which vary with the sunspot cycle.

10 Suppose that you are engaged in research. You are engaged, let us say, in investigating some aspect of scientific medicine. The work is difficult and is likely to absorb the whole of your intellectual energy. You have not time to consider the effects which your

discoveries may have outside the field of medicine. You succeed, let us suppose, in enormously lowering the infant death-rate. This has the entirely unintended result of making the food supply inadequate and lowering the standard of life in the most populous parts of the world.

Exercise 160

Find, from any existing modern texts available to you, twenty pairs of sentences linked by sentence connecters, and list the sentence connecters you have found.

Pro-forms

Exercise 161

Reply in the affirmative to each of the questions below, using a pro-form for the part of the sentence underlined, as in the following model:

A Do you have a book?
B Yes, I have one.

1 Do you have any stamps?
2 Have you seen both of those plays?
3 Is it true that each man had a gun?
4 Is it true that every man was armed?
5 Are there enough seats for everyone?
6 I have your ticket. Do you have my ticket?
7 Is it true that there are no seats left?
8 Is that the only loaf you have left?
9 Were all the other tickets sold?
10 Did other people hear what he said, too?
11 Is this the same table that we ate at yesterday?
12 Is this the same soup that they gave us yesterday?
13 Is that the waiter who served us?
14 Is the man in the corner the man you mean?
15 Have you studied the menu yet?
16 Are these gloves your gloves?
17 Is it true that this is the very bed he died in?
18 The population of China is far greater than the population of Japan.
19 Forests in Russia are far more extensive than the forests of western Europe.
20 Have you answered all of these questions?

Exercise 162

Reply in the affirmative to the questions below, using a pro-form for the phrase underlined:

1 Will you be in your room tomorrow morning?

2 Will you be in your room tomorrow morning?
3 If we meet tomorrow morning, will tomorrow morning be convenient for you?
4 If we meet in your room, will your room be all right?
5 Can I get to Boston by taking this side road?
6 Is it all right if I pronounce 'clothes' omitting the 'th' sound?

Pro-forms for the predicate

Exercise 163

Give a detailed analysis, in terms used in the *Grammar,* of the pro-forms used by B in the exchanges below. For example, in the exchange

A Are you ready?
B Yes, I am,

am is used as a pro-form for the first person singular, present tense, of BE, plus complement:

1 A Is Tom still waiting?
B Yes, he is.
2 A Have you any matches?
B Yes, I have.
3 A John has a cold.
B I think he has.
4 A Robert has a car.
B I think he does.
5 A Has he passed his driving test?
B Yes, he has.
6 A He can drive very well.
B I'm sure he can.
7 A In fact, he drives very carefully.
B I agree, he does.
8 A You drive well yourself.
B I *did.*
9 A Have you been swimming?
B Yes, I have.
10 A Have you been swimming?
B Yes, I have been.
11 A I haven't seen the exhibition.
B Well, you should.
12 A I haven't seen it either.
B Oh, you should have.
13 A I didn't see it.
B But you should have.
14 A Need we wait?
B Yes, you must.

15 A I haven't met June.
B But you must have.
16 A I'm not a member of the club.
B But you must be.
17 A I'll be there this evening.
B So will I.
18 A Theodore will be there.
B So he will.
19 A May I take this chair?
B Please do.
20 A I'm going to open the window.
B No, don't.

Exercise 164
Study the following models:

a A Do you like chocolate?
B I did. But I don't now.
b A Do you ride a bicycle?
B I did. But I don't do so now.
c A Did you write that slogan on the wall?
B No, I didn't do that.

Note: in b, *do so* is optional; and in c, *that* is replaceable by *it*. Now, on the pattern of one of B's responses above, provide an answer to the questions below; use *do so, do that* or *do it* whenever possible:

1 Do you go swimming every day?
2 Did you believe in ghosts?
3 Did you cut down that cherry tree?
4 Do you understand how a computer works?
5 Do you have breakfast in bed?
6 Did you throw all this paper on the floor?
7 Do you feel giddy?
8 Do you open your bedroom window every night?

Pro-forms for non-finite clauses

Exercise 165
Study the following models:

a A Do you want to go home?
B Yes, I want to (do so).
b A Would you like me to take you home?
B Yes, I would like you to (do so).
c A Do you enjoy swimming?
B Yes, I enjoy it.

d A Did you see him opening the safe?
B Yes, I saw him (doing so).

Note that *do so* is optional in a and b, and that *doing so* is optional in d. Now, on the pattern of one of B's responses above, provide an answer to these questions:

1 Did you remember to post that letter?
2 Would you prefer to stay here?
3 Do you wish to make a formal complaint?
4 Would you advise me to see a lawyer?
5 Did you really expect him to tell you the truth?
6 Do you trust me to keep my word?
7 Do you advise consulting a lawyer?
8 Did you regret selling that picture?
9 Did you really catch him smoking opium?
10 Do you often see him doing shadow boxing?

Pro-forms for *that*-clauses

Exercise 166

Study the following models:

a A Is it true that the war has ended?
B Everyone says so.
b A Do you think it will start again?
B I hope not.

On the pattern of B's response, provide first an affirmative answer, then a negative one, to the questions below, using the verb in brackets:

1 Is Thompson going to be re-elected? (think)
2 Will there be a re-election? (believe)
3 Will the elections take place next month? (imagine)
4 Will we all have to vote again? (suppose)
5 Will there be an announcement in the press tomorrow? (assume)
6 Did something go wrong with the last election then? (it appears)

Various uses of *so* as a pro-form

Exercise 167

Explain the grammatical function of *so* in the following examples:

1 A Is there going to be a general election?
B I believe so.
2 A There's going to be a general election.
B So I believe.
C So do I.
3 He folded his hands in the traditional greeting: so did the monkey.

4 A The road's closed. We can't get through.
  B I told you so, didn't I?
5 A You told her the secret.
  B That isn't so.
6 Many people are dominated by machines, but I do not wish to be so.
7 The cook was not naturally fat, but he soon became so.
8 You say you are a doctor, but you are not so described in these papers.
9 A I would like to volunteer, sir.
  B Are you really prepared to do so?
10 I thought a typewriter would be necessary, so I taught myself to type.

Anaphoric and cataphoric reference

Exercise 168

Find the examples of discourse reference in the sentences below, and say whether each example is of anaphoric or cataphoric reference:

1 Find examples of discourse reference in the following sentences.
2 The chief came to New York when he was well past sixty. He flew over here, rocketed, as it were, in a matter of hours.
3 When I was nineteen, I left my native village. That was more than fifteen years ago.
4 When I reached home, I found that the whole house had been ransacked. This convinced me that I had enemies somewhere.
5 You want to know where we stand. This is the position. We are surrounded on all sides, but have ammunition to withstand any attack.
6 The above example is purely fictitious. What follows is authentic.
7 This is part of a transcript of a recorded interview:
  'You said in your last broadcast that, if there were fewer cars in our cities, the buses would be able to give better service. But isn't that hypothesis quite unrealistic?'
8 Six hundred and fifty people voted against the proposal. The Committee had not expected such opposition, and hurriedly withdrew to reconsider their next move.

Ellipsis in dialogue

Exercise 169

Answer the questions below in the affirmative in the following five ways: a. including the whole of the predication contained in the question; b. including the predication but with a pro-form for Od; c. with a pro-form for the predication; d. using only the operator as a pro-form for the predicate; e. ellipting the subject and predicate altogether. Each of the five answers should contain *Yes*.

1 Have you answered that letter?
2 Has John paid this account?

3 Has he asked for a receipt?
4 Will they send back the cheque?

Now repeat all the answers, replacing *Yes* in 1 by *Of course,* in 2 by *probably,* in 3 by *perhaps,* and in 4 by *eventually*.

Exercise 170

In the same five ways as in Exercise 169, answer the following questions so that each of the five answers contains the adverbial(s) in brackets:

1 When did you answer that letter? (yesterday)
2 When did John pay this account? (probably, on Friday)
3 How often do you attend his lectures? (usually, twice a week)
4 How soon will they take away this rubbish? (perhaps, tomorrow)

Exercise 171

Provide suitable rejoinders, containing ellipsis, for each of the utterances reported below. Give one rejoinder to each utterance in the form of a question, then one rejoinder for each in the form of a statement:

1 Don't worry, John has paid the bill.
2 I have had a word with the manager.
3 They will take all this luggage away.
4 I go to the dentist every week.
5 We paid six hundred dollars for that picture.

11 The complex sentence

Dependent clauses

Exercise 172

Isolate and label the dependent clause or clauses in each of the sentences below, as in the following two models,

a I think you can do it.

You can do it: finite clause acting as O in the superordinate clause.

b Leaving the room, he tripped over the mat.

Leaving the room: non-finite, *-ing* participle clause, acting as A in the superordinate clause,

using the symbols S (=subject), O (=object), C (=complement), A (=adjunct).

1 That you could do it I always knew.
2 That you can do it is still uncertain.
3 You can do it if you try.
4 If you can do it, I'll give you ten dollars.
5 Standing here all day, I see many strange faces.
6 Standing here all day is extremely tiring.
7 My greatest pleasure is to listen to chamber music.
8 To listen to chamber music is my greatest pleasure.
9 Exhausted after the long journey, I fell asleep at once.
10 The long journey over, we relaxed in the warm sunshine.
11 Glancing up at my tired face, she asked, in a rather grating voice, how I was feeling.
12 Steinweg had a large room where we always breakfasted together.
13 He was a delightful companion, always cheerful and considerate.
14 She had not asked life to be thus.
15 She sang when allowed to do so.
16 She sang completely out of tune, so that permission was seldom granted.
17 What he saw both surprised and frightened him.
18 Since I have been especially invited to speak, for you now to tell me I cannot do so is quite unpardonable.

19 Having been invited to speak, and then being told to keep silent, I shall never come here again as long as I live.

20 What I wanted to say was, as I didn't know whether you were going to say that you could come or you couldn't, could you make it the following Saturday?

Exercise 173

Items 11, 18, 19 and 20 of Exercise 172 contain more than one dependent clause. Label each of these dependent clauses, eg *a, b, c,* etc. Analyse each clause, e.g. S, V, O, C, A, and explain in what way each one is dependent on the main clause or on one of the other dependent clauses in the sentence.

Exercise 174

The non-finite clauses in the sentences below are open to more than one interpretation. Illustrate this by expanding each dependent clause in two different ways:

1 I ran over a dog crossing the square.

2 To see her alone would be very indiscreet.

3 Though shouting as loudly as possible, the rescuers could not hear us.

4 Dressed in white robes, we thought the visitors looked like priests in some strange ceremony.

5 I regret speaking to you so bluntly.

6 Walking fast after breakfast could be fatal.

7 He was so ill as to be obliged to give up work altogether.

8 It will take several hours to finish this.

9 Whether here or not, his application will have to be considered.

10 Always afraid of snakes, we shut every door and window at night.

Exercise 175

Pick out the indicators of subordination in the twenty sentences of Exercise 172.

Exercise 176

Classify the words underlined in the following sentences as either prepositions or subordinators:

1 I am speaking to you as your doctor.

2 You talk exactly as a doctor does.

3 Since leaving school, I have travelled round the world.

4 I haven't been back to my old school since I came up to university.

5 Since the beginning of the year, I haven't written a single essay.

6 Take two of the tablets before going to bed.

7 Take two more before breakfast next morning.

8 I will not go near her house until she sends me a written explanation.

9 With so many people chatting, it was impossible to hear what the speaker was trying to say.

10 I can't work in a room with so many other people.
11 He would never put himself out for anybody.
12 For anybody to pretend such a thing is nonsense.

Exercise 177

Classify *the function of the dependent clauses* in the sentences below under the following headings:

a subject
b direct object
c subject complement
d indirect object
e object complement
f appositive
g adjunct
h disjunct
i conjunct
j postmodifier in noun phrase
k prepositional complement
l adjectival complement

1 As the sun went down behind the church, the trees suddenly became still.
2 I was terrified, to tell you the truth.
3 One afternoon I was sitting on the wall dividing our house from the churchyard.
4 In daylight, I thought of the Roman remains that had been dug up under our house.
5 Walking along from St Mary's, you come to a high wall.
6 You find the wall heightens suddenly.
7 We found the wall overgrown with ivy.
8 What I remember most of that evening is the reasonableness of my father's arguments.
9 The truth is that I really liked him.
10 The truth, that I really wanted to learn, suddenly dawned on my poor father.
11 What is more important, I suddenly felt ashamed of my childishness.
12 My father was sure that I would overcome my fears.
13 He strongly disapproved of what I had been doing.
14 Now I often meet men who were once at school with me.
15 Whenever I encounter one of them, I feel an outsider.
16 However, seeing George again has left me much more confident.

Nominal clauses

Exercise 178

Which of the sentences below contain nominal *that*-clauses?

1 Everyone tends to think that he is not sufficiently appreciated.
2 Everyone that thinks so is not necessarily conceited.
3 My opinion that you disagree with so strongly has not been properly represented.
4 My opinion, that no action need be taken yet, is shared by most of us here.

5 The main difficulty lies in the fact that we have nobody properly qualified for this work.
6 We are at a serious disadvantage in that we have nobody properly qualified for this work.
7 I understand you have had some trouble with your telephone.
8 You've had some trouble with your telephone, I understand.
9 That John actually took the money, I can't believe.
10 John never actually took the money, I believe.

Exercise 179

Combine each of the pairs of sentences below so as to form one sentence containing a nominal *that*-clause. Say in each case whether the subordinator *that* is optional or obligatory; and say what function the *that*-clause is fulfilling in the superordinate clause:

1 We have only enough water for two more days. I told you so.
2 We have only enough for two days. I am very sorry.
3 We have only enough for two days. That is our conclusion.
4 In view of the drought, there is only enough water for two days. That is our conclusion.
5 We have only enough for two days. I estimate that having taken very careful measurements.
6 We have only enough for two days. That is very alarming.
7 We conclude that there is only enough for two days. Our conclusion has been reached after very careful checking.
8 We cannot stay here. We must face that fact.
9 I am convinced we cannot stay here. The results will be disastrous if we do.
10 We have almost exhausted our supplies. How can I convince you of that?

Exercise 180

Combine each of the pairs of sentences below so as to form one sentence containing a *wh*-clause. Say what function the *wh*-clause is fulfilling in the superordinate clause:

1 What caused the explosion? No one ever discovered.
2 What damage did the explosion cause? It took three weeks to estimate.
3 Where did the fire start? That was a complete mystery.
4 When did the fever begin? The seriousness of his condition depends on that.
5 When did the fever begin? I am not quite sure.
6 Which drawer does he keep his money in? I can never remember.
7 How can we reduce this high temperature? My problem is that.
8 Why didn't he say he was feeling ill? The question is irrelevant at this stage.
9 How often do these fevers occur? I cannot tell you that precisely.
10 How much will all this cost? I am concerned about that.

Exercise 181

Replace the finite *wh*-clause by an infinitive *wh*-clause whenever possible. Then give a full and accurate statement of the restrictions on the formation of an infinitive *wh*-clause:

1 I never know where I ought to put my coat.
2 Where I ought to put my coat I never know.
3 I can't tell you where you can put your coat.
4 Can you tell me where the guests can put their coats?
5 I can't remember where I put my coat yesterday.
6 Can anyone tell me what I must do now?
7 Does anyone know how one can open this safe?
8 Someone will tell us when we should start.
9 Someone will tell us when the concert will end.
10 Will somebody tell me why I must fill up this form?

Exercise 182

Combine each of the pairs of questions below so as to form one question containing a dependent *yes-no* clause. When both *if* and *whether* would be acceptable, say so.

1 Are you really enjoying yourself? I wonder.
2 Are you really enjoying yourself? He asked me.
3 Are you enjoying yourself or not? I don't care.
4 Does it cost too much? That depends on how badly you want it.
5 Does it cost too much? My decision will depend on that.
6 Is it too expensive or not? That is the crucial question.
7 Can it be easily resold? I'm not interested.
8 Is it properly insured? I am not sure.

Nominal relative clauses

Exercise 183

Say which of the *wh*-clauses below are *wh*-interrogative clauses, and which are nominal relative clauses:

1 What caused the fire remains a mystery.
2 What caused the fire was a cigarette end.
3 We never discovered what caused the fire.
4 Who first reported the fire is still uncertain.
5 Whoever reported the fire was only doing his duty.
6 Can you tell me where your friends are?
7 Home is where your friends and family are.
8 Do you remember when Columbus discovered America?
9 Do you remember when we first came here, darling?
10 What we all need is a spell of warm sunshine.

Exercise 184
Illustrate, by paraphrase, the difference between *a* and *b* in each of the following pairs of sentences:

1 a I'll give you what you want.
  b I'll give you whatever you want.
2 a Where I sit in the evening is very quiet.
  b Wherever I sit in the evening is someone else's chair.
3 a Come and see me when you can.
  b Come and see me whenever you can.
4 a Tell me how much you need.
  b I'll give you however much you need.
5 a Who told you that, I wonder.
  b Whoever told you that was not telling the truth.

Nominal *to*-infinitive clauses
Exercise 185
Say (a) what function the infinitive clause fulfils in the superordinate clause below; and (b) what is the subject of each of the two clauses:

1 I expect to be there this evening.
2 I expect everyone to be punctual this evening.
3 I promise you not to be late.
4 The plan is for us all to meet outside at eight.
5 The plan for us all to meet outside was absurd.
6 To speak in public for the first time can be a terrifying experience.
7 For Osbert to appear in public at such a time was rather courageous.

Nominal *-ing* clauses
Exercise 186
Say what function the *-ing* clauses fulfil in the superordinate clauses below:

1 I always enjoy listening to chamber music.
2 Listening to chamber music is my greatest pleasure.
3 His greatest pleasure, climbing mountains, had to be abandoned.
4 Was he, then, so given to climbing mountains?
5 He was always happy scaling almost perpendicular cliffs.

Exercise 187
Rephrase these sentences, using an *-ing* participle preceded by a personal pronoun or noun in the genitive case:

1 We all are surprised that he made that mistake.
2 He was an astronaut and that accounted for the size of the audience.
3 No one will object if you finish the lecture a little early.

4 Would you approve if I had this article copied?
5 We did not realize that Walker would cause so much trouble by speaking to the press.
6 The fact that he has spoken to the press about this has caused us a good deal of embarrassment.
7 Do you mind if I don't come with you?
8 We had not been told of the meeting till yesterday and that meant that we did not have sufficient time to prepare our case properly.

Adverbial clauses: time

Exercise 188

Reduce the finite time clauses to non-finite or verbless time clauses whenever such reduction would be acceptable without change of voice.

1 When I last saw you, you lived in Washington.
2 When you lived in Washington, did you ever meet Robert H. Davidson?
3 Since I met you, I have been reading your book.
4 Once your book is published, it will sell very rapidly.
5 When you are in Rome, do as Rome does.
6 Until you are asked to speak, you would be well advised to remain silent.
7 Before he served in the army, he was much too fat.
8 While he was in the army, he learnt a great deal about electricity.
9 When you enter the town, you will see the monument straight in front of you.
10 After he had travelled round the world, Forbes settled down peacefully in his native village.

Time clauses introduced by *until*

Exercise 189

Fill the gaps in the following sentences by either (a) *until* or (b) *by the time that:*

1 Please wait ______ I return.
2 Don't wait ______ I come back.
3 ______ I come back, I want you to be on your way.
4 They had left ______ we returned.
5 It was dark ______ they arrived.
6 They did not arrive ______ it was dark.
7 We rode hard ______ it was dark.
8 Don't pour the water in ______ it is boiling.
9 The water was boiling ______ the electricity failed.
10 The electricity was not cut off ______ the water boiled.

Adverbial clauses: conditional and concessive

Exercise 190

Combine each of the pairs of sentences below so as to form a single sentence containing a conditional or a concessive clause:

1 Stand up here. Then you can see the mountains clearly.
2 Stand up. Otherwise you won't be able to see anything.
3 Stand up here. That is the only way you can see anything.
4 We strained our eyes. But we couldn't see anything.
5 You can strain your eyes. But still you won't be able to see anything.
6 You could have the best binoculars in the world. But still you wouldn't be able to see anything more.
7 I will let you come with me on one condition. You must do exactly what I tell you.
8 I am sure this story is untrue. Otherwise, it would be an absolute scandal.
9 I am sure that never really happened. Otherwise, we would all be dead by now.
10 You might need some help at some time. Then you must let me know.
11 All you had to do was telephone me. Then I would have come round at once.
12 It doesn't matter what I say. He always does something different.
13 You can tell me or not. But in any case I will find out the truth.
14 I have no idea what the solution is. But we shall certainly find it.
15 His difficulties were very great indeed. But he always overcame them in the end.

Adverbial clauses: reason, cause, circumstance

Exercise 191

Which of the dependent clauses in the sentences below are adjuncts, and which are disjuncts? Which of the adjunct clauses express (a) reason or cause, and which express (b) circumstance:

1 They've lit a fire, because they're so cold.
2 They've lit a fire, because I can smell smoke.
3 Since you ask me, I think you're being unwise.
4 We'd better start the meeting, as we have a quorum.
5 Because there was no quorum, the Chairman ruled that the meeting must be reconvened.
6 There being no quorum, the meeting was postponed.
7 Since everyone appears to be present, the meeting can now begin.
8 Seeing that you live next door to Mr Roberts, you ought to be able to recognize him.

Adverbial clauses: purpose and result

Exercise 192

If the infinitive clause in the sentences below are clauses of purpose, answer *Yes*; and in that case replace *to* by *so as to* or *in order to*:

1 The Minister continued to address his audience.

2 The Minister stopped to address the bystanders.
3 I wanted to ask him a question.
4 I waited to ask him a question.
5 He invited me to come to his office.
6 He invited me to keep me happy.
7 He left us to catch his plane.
8 He left us to go our own way.
9 He encouraged us to visit him again.
10 He encouraged us to win our support.

Exercise 193
Which of the dependent clauses below express (a) purpose, and which express (b) result?

1 The police used a loud-hailer so that everyone in the building heard them.
2 They used a loud-hailer so that everyone could hear them.
3 So that everyone could hear, they used a loud-hailer.
4 We planted hundreds of roses, so that the garden should look beautiful at the time of the wedding.
5 We watered the garden thoroughly, so that it smelt fresh when the guests arrived.

Adverbial clauses: manner
Exercise 194
Fill the gaps by
as   as if   as though   in the way that   in any way (that)
the way

1 Do ______ I say and not ______ I do.
2 I can't play the guitar ______ you do.
3 He writes ______ he is left-handed.
4 He played ______ he was inspired.
5 He talks to me ______ he were my grandfather.
6 Answer the question ______ you think suitable.
7 Answer this question ______ you think most suitable.

Adverbial clauses: proportion and preference
Exercise 195
Supply a suitable subordinator:

1 ______ you sow, ______ you will reap.
2 The sooner we start, ______ we'll get there.
3 ______ they drew nearer to the coast, they found the land less barren, the air more humid.

4 ______ leave this paradise, they decided to settle there for ever.
5 They preferred to build houses of stone, ______ using wood from such trees as there were.

'Unattached' clauses

Exercise 196

Say which of the dependent clauses below are unacceptable, and rephrase each sentence concerned:

1 Speaking frankly, the situation is worse than we feared.
2 Speaking clearly, everyone at the back of the hall could hear what I was saying.
3 When fully grown, these trees are a magnificent sight.
4 When fully grown, the men cut off all the lower branches.
5 Grazing by the river, we suddenly came across a fine herd of cattle.
6 Before retiring, take two of these pills with a little water.
7 Shouting slogans, the streets were thronged with indignant workmen.
8 Considering the weather is so uncertain, the reception will be held indoors.

Comparative sentences

Exercise 197

Indicate, by S, Cs, Od, Oi or A, the comparative element in the following sentences:

1 Man has greater power over his environment than he has ever had before.
2 More has been discovered about the universe in the last fifty years than in all the previous centuries.
3 Technology has given more people than ever the means of leading a comfortable and easy life.
4 Science has progressed more rapidly in the last few decades than in hundreds of years before.
5 Yet are we really happier than our ancestors were?

Exercise 198

In what ways are the following sentences ambiguous, and how could the ambiguity be removed?

1 We have greater power over our environment than our fathers.
2 There were more intelligent astrologers than you young scientists.
3 We need more highly trained scientists.

***Enough* and *too* + infinitive**

Exercise 199

Say whether the element underlined in the following sentences is subject or object of the infinitive clause, noting that in two cases it can be either.

1 John is too ill to get up.
2 He is too ill to move.
3 He is not well enough to go out.
4 That fence is too high to jump.
5 That horse is not strong enough to jump yet.
6 This tea is too hot to drink.
7 I am feeling much too hot to eat.
8 This writing is too faint to read.
9 Mary is too faint to stand up.
10 Thomas is too stupid to teach.

Exercise 200

a Using the information contained in the following two sentences,
Burke was a very eloquent speaker. He convinced even the most sceptical of his opponents,
form ten single sentences using the constructions below:

1 . . . so eloquent that . . .
2 . . . so eloquent a speaker that . . .
3 . . . so eloquently that . . .
4 . . . such an eloquent . . .
5 . . . so eloquent as to . . .
6 . . . was such as to . . .
7 So eloquent . . .
8 So eloquently . . .
9 Such was . . .
10 With such . . .

b Make up ten original sentences on the same models.

Comment clauses

Exercise 201

If the underlined part of each of the following sentences constitutes a comment clause, answer *Yes,* and then explain in what way the clause functions:

1 I told you Burke was an eloquent speaker.
2 Burke was an eloquent speaker, I told you.
3 Burke, I told you, was an eloquent speaker.
4 His audience listened spellbound as he spoke.
5 His audience listened spellbound, as I said.
6 What some of them were thinking, I can well imagine.
7 What were they really thinking, I wonder?
8 Burke endeavoured, in all his speeches, to be sincere.
9 Sometimes, to be sincere, I felt that his eloquence concealed the real truth.
10 What is important, he believed passionately in the cause he was upholding.
11 What is important for him was this passionate belief.
12 Speaking as a patriot, he succeeded in arousing patriotic feelings in the most self-seeking members of his audience.
13 Speaking as a patriot is always a popular course when one's country is threatened.

14 Speaking as a patriot, I feel that he is playing a dangerous game.
15 Summed up in words of one syllable, he is a fool.
16 Summed up in simple language, his speech meant nothing at all.
17 You may remember you told me about your trip to Vienna.
18 You told me about your trip to Vienna, you may remember.
19 You told me, you may remember, that you saw Frances there.
20 I remember, you told me she was travelling with her cousin.
21 Was it really her cousin, I wonder?

Exercise 202
Read the 21 sentences in Exercise 201 aloud, then comment on the difference in intonation between (a) the sentences that contain a comment clause and those that do not, and (b) the sentences in which a comment clause comes at the end and those in which such a clause comes elsewhere.

Tenses in dependent clauses
Exercise 203
From each of the pairs of sentences below, form one single sentence containing a clause beginning with one of the following subordinators:

if unless when as soon as after before in case

1 Perhaps you will arrive at your hotel before five o'clock. In that case, please telephone me at my office.
2 I will leave a message for you with my secretary. It is possible that I will be out when you telephone.
3 Perhaps I will have left my office when you arrive. In that case, please telephone me at my house.
4 I will discuss your programme with you. Do not make any appointments before that.
5 We will first agree on your programme. Immediately after that, you can start making appointments.
6 I wish to approve of any appointments you make. You must not make any otherwise.
7 You will be free to go sightseeing. However, you will have to finish all your work first.
8 Perhaps you will not carry out all your programme. Then you will have to come back next week.
9 You will perhaps run into difficulties. If that should happen, do not proceed, but consult me first.
10 You will perhaps run into difficulties. Otherwise, I will not interfere.

Exercise 204
In each of the following exchanges of conversation, expand B's reply so that

it contains a dependent clause with a verb in the modal past, but contains only information already supplied or implied by A:

1 A Do you think we should leave now?
  B Yes, it's time.
2 A John thinks he knows all the answers.
  B Yes, he talks like it.
3 A John is not in charge of this department.
  B No, but he behaves like it.
4 A Shall we stop now?
  B I'd rather not.
5 A This isn't our own home, you know.
  B No, but let's suppose otherwise.
6 A Wouldn't you like to have enough money to buy a yacht?
  B Indeed, if only . . .
7 A What a pity George isn't here!
  B Yes, we could really have fun.
8 A It was a good thing the police didn't stop you.
  B Yes, I would have been in trouble.
9 A But for that old lady's hat, we could see the stage perfectly.
  B Yes, we could see very well.
10 A I'm sorry I stepped on the cat.
  B Yes, my wife would never have heard us otherwise.

Tenses with *since*

Exercise 205

Combine each of the following pairs of sentences so as to form one single sentence, using *since* as a subordinator and not using the material in brackets:

1 My parents came to live here (in 1965). (From that point of time), they have been much better in health.
2 They have lived here (throughout a period of time). (During that period), they have made many new friends.
3 John left Anne (two weeks ago). (From that moment), she has hardly eaten anything.
4 Anne has been in the house by herself (for two weeks). (During that time), she has refused to open the door to anyone.
5 I heard that song (the day before yesterday). (Subsequently), it has been ringing in my ears (all the time).
6 Robert was living in Rome (three years ago). (Between then and now) I have not had a word from him.
7 George began listening to English recordings regularly (last October). His pronunciation is (now) greatly improved.
8 He has been listening to English recordings (for several months). He is (now) not spending so much time playing cards.

The subjunctive

Exercise 206

Change the verb phrase in the dependent finite clause so as to use the subjunctive.

1 I propose, Mr Chairman, that the Committee should adjourn and should meet again tomorrow.
2 We have already decided that this meeting should be adjourned until tomorrow.
3 If this report is true, then the situation is indeed very serious.
4 If this report was more accurate, it would be an invaluable document.
5 Though there may be some inaccuracies in this report, we must consider it very seriously.
6 The author of this report has written it as if he alone was in possession of the facts.
7 Suppose every word of this was true, what action would the Committee wish to take?
8 If the truth is known to any of you, it must be told to us all.
9 If the truth was known, there would be a public outcry.
10 Whatever may be the difficulties before us, we must face them with courage and determination.

Putative *should*

Exercise 207

Rephrase the sentences below, using putative *should* whenever possible:

1 I gather that you are worried about the expense.
2 I am sorry that you have any doubts about our ability to keep expenditure under control.
3 We deeply regret that we must take this action.
4 It is quite right for you to speak in your defence.
5 It is quite right that Jones stole the key.
6 I am surprised at your saying such a thing.
7 I can't imagine why you insist on his innocence.
8 Isn't it possible that somebody else stole it?
9 What I cannot understand is why he refused to answer my question.
10 That stories of this kind are published in the press is a disgrace to our society.

Indirect speech

Exercise 208

Rewrite the following two narratives, after the second sentence in each case, using indirect speech throughout:

a Three days later, the monkeys were still infesting my house, practically tearing the place apart. That afternoon a friend came back from a business trip.
'I know the answer,' he said. 'You need a Pied Piper.'
'All right. Find me one.'
'All you have to do is send a boy down to the city, to this address.'

b William Plomer disliked telephones. He once told this story. He said 'I heard a well-known actor on the radio yesterday. He was asked: "Suppose you were left alone on a desert island and you were allowed to take just one luxury with you, what would you choose?" "I should take a telephone," he said, "and I should push the wire into the sand, and my greatest pleasure would be to sit and look at it, and to think: It will never ring and I shall never have to answer it."'

Exercise 209
The extract below is taken from a radio interview. Rewrite it in reported speech, beginning *The interviewer asked . . .*

Interviewer: Dr Schaller, is it true that you have been living for over a year with gorillas?
Dr Schaller: Yes, that is quite true.
Interviewer: How long did you spend with your gorillas in all?
Dr Schaller: I was in Africa for a term of twenty months. The gorillas soon became quite used to my presence, and when I arrived at the edge of their group, they looked up and then usually continued with their daily routine.
Interviewer: They live in groups, do they?
Dr Schaller: Yes. Each group consists of from five to thirty animals.

Free indirect speech

Exercise 210
Rephrase the following paragraph, after the second sentence, in free indirect speech:

Forster looked about him. He was all alone on a dark,cold railway platform. 'Where am I?' he thought. 'This is Nassenheide, isn't it? Or have I left the train at the wrong station? No, I haven't. There, in the dim lamp-light, I can see the sign: Nassenheide. Then why is there no one to meet me? Surely they must have had my telegram! How can they leave me to find my own way, with all my luggage, in this pitch darkness and driving rain? Well, I will put my suitcases in the waiting-room, and walk. But where shall I walk to? I remember now. They wrote to tell me the house was up the hill about a mile from the station. Even then, I can't believe they expected me to find my way to a strange house on a night like this.'

12 The verb and its complementation

Phrasal verbs, prepositional verbs, phrasal-prepositional verbs

Exercise 211

The structure of the verb phrase can be analysed in a number of ways, including the following:

a	verb + particle	eg	sat down
b	v. + prepositional phrase	,,	ran across the road
c	v. + particle + prep. phrase	,,	set off on a journey
d	v. + prepositional adverb	,,	ran across
e	v. + prep. adv. + prep. phrase	,,	go across to the baker's
f	transitive phrasal v. + object	,,	find out the truth
g	prepositional v. + object	,,	looked at me
h	phrasal-prepositional v. + obj.	,,	put up with him

Indicate, by *a, b, c,* etc., in which of those eight ways the verb phrase in each of the sentences below can be analysed:

1 I went into the dining room.
2 We went into the matter carefully.
3 We must call in the police.
4 The police will call in a car.
5 I rushed out of the house.
6 I rushed out.
7 I drove out to my friends.
8 They all trooped off.
9 They all set off down the road.
10 He flew across the Atlantic.
11 We flew across in no time.
12 How long can one do without water?
13 Has anyone rung up?
14 Has anyone rung me up?
15 Don't come down.
16 Don't give up.
17 Don't give me away.
18 You must face up to your responsibilities.
19 You must come up to my office.
20 We must make up for lost time.
21 Will you come up for a cup of tea?
22 The train has passed over the bridge.
23 It has passed over safely.
24 The selection committee has passed you over.
25 My hat has fallen off.
26 The plane has taken off.
27 The actor took the President off beautifully.
28 Go onto the platform.
29 Go on to the next town.
30 You must cut down on cigarettes.

Exercise 212

Replace the object in each of these sentences by the corresponding pronoun; then give the whole new sentence:

1 Back up the hill.
2 Back up your friends.
3 Call off the game.
4 Come off my bed.
5 Get over the wall.
6 Get this meeting over.
7 Swim across the river.
8 Put across this message.
9 Run in the race.
10 Run in the engine.
11 Step up this ladder.
12 Step up production.
13 You take after your father.
14 I took to John at once.
15 You can take over my job.
16 Don't turn on the light.
17 The dog turned on the stranger.
18 Turn down this street.
19 Turn down his proposal.
20 Now wind up your watch.

Exercise 213

Say whether the adverb, in brackets, could fit into position *a, b, c* or *d*. Note that more than one position may be possible.

1 They looked [a] at [b] the picture [c] (carefully)
2 They turned [a] on [b] the gas [c] (slowly)
3 They turned [a] the gas [b] on [c] (slowly)
4 He's catching [a] up [b] with [c] the leaders [d] (quickly)
5 Go [a] on [b] to the end [c] (right)
6 The negotiations have [a] broken [b] down [c] (completely)
7 The crowd made [a] for [b] shelter [c] (hurriedly)
8 The Spartans brought [a] their children [b] up [c] (strictly)
9 I'll look [a] into [b] your complaint [c] (immediately)
10 He puts [a] up [b] with [c] any inconvenience [d] (patiently)

Exercise 214

Change the position of the word underlined, if it is mobile:

1 The Spartans brought up their children strictly.
2 Lester gradually caught up with the leaders.
3 I don't want to break up the party.
4 The meeting broke up in disorder.
5 We must hurry to make up for lost time.
6 Please send this telegram off urgently.
7 Please get that parcel off at once.
8 Why don't you take off your coat?
9 We must find out the answer somehow.
10 Be careful. Don't run over that child.

Exercise 215
Put into the passive, supplying the *by*-phrase only if it contains relevant and essential information.

1 I will bring up this question at our next meeting.
2 We shall then deal with it more fully.
3 Have you looked into this matter?
4 The facts do not bear out your argument.
5 No one has ever looked after this house properly.
6 Is anybody attending to you?
7 They have turned down my application.
8 Thieves broke into the National Bank last night.
9 The citizens set upon any foreigner, however innocent.
10 You must get on with this job immediately.

Exercise 216
Transform each of the sentences below in the following way:

I was looking for that book ~
That is the book I was looking for.

1 We were just talking about that article.
2 Queen Elizabeth slept in this bed.
3 I want to back out of that agreement.
4 I want you to break down those figures.
5 I think we should leave this sentence out.
6 We have not yet dealt with this paragraph.
7 We must now see to this matter.
8 I was looking forward to that film.
9 We must cut down on these expenses.
10 You should get on with this job first.

Exercise 217
Read the answers to Exercises 215 and 216 aloud. Then comment on the stress and intonation.

'Current' and 'resulting' copulas
Exercise 218
Indicate, by *a, b, c,* etc., which of the following copulas could fill the gap in each of the sentences below:

a appear
b be
c become
d feel
e get
f go
g grow
h look
i make
j remain
k seem
l smell
m sound
n taste
o turn

1 Marie Curie ______ a famous scientist.
2 She ______ devoted to her work.
3 The work ______ more and more interesting.
4 This chair ______ comfortable.
5 The milk ______ sour.
6 My coffee ______ rather sweet.
7 John ______ a very good husband.
8 The weather ______ much warmer.
9 The poor old woman ______ mad.
10 She ______ thin and wizened.
11 These four books ______ for you.
12 The concert ______ at six o'clock.
13 He ______ rather a fool.
14 Everyone ______ in the garden.
15 That he crossed the desert alone ______ unbelievable.

Complementation of the adjective phrase

Exercise 219

Supply an acceptable preposition to fill each of the gaps. If an adjectival complement is structurally optional in the context, put brackets round it, thus:

Most people are afraid (of snakes)

If the complement is structurally obligatory in the context, omit the brackets:

1 We're accustomed ______ noise.
2 George is ahead ______ me.
3 Are you angry ______ us?
4 I'm not answerable ______ anyone.
5 John is anxious ______ Mary.
6 Aren't you ashamed ______ yourself?
7 Jack is averse ______ hard work.
8 I'm well aware ______ that.
9 Now we're bound ______ home.
10 I'm busy ______ my accounts.
11 George is capable ______ anything.
12 Are you certain ______ success?
13 We're not clear ______ this sentence.
14 John is concerned ______ Mary.
15 Who is concerned ______ this project?
16 We're conscious ______ the danger.
17 Jane is crazy ______ dancing.
18 The judge was deaf ______ our appeal.
19 Mary is very dear ______ us.
20 She is so dependent ______ us.
21 Chalk is different ______ cheese.
22 When is John due ______ promotion?
23 He is eager ______ more responsibility.
24 Don't be envious ______ anyone.
25 He is not equal ______ the task.
26 He's not expert ______ anything.
27 Have you been faithful ______ me?
28 I'm not familiar ______ this town.
29 Fred is not fit ______ this job.

30 John is fond ______ Mary.
31 I'm glad ______ your prize.
32 I'd be glad ______ a rest.
33 John is good ______ chemistry.
34 We're grateful ______ your help.
35 We're grateful ______ you.
36 Don't be too hard ______ me.
37 He's hungry ______ knowledge.
38 I'm ignorant ______ those facts.
39 Be independent ______ others.
40 Don't feel inferior ______ anyone.
41 John is intent ______ his work.
42 Are you jealous ______ her?
43 I'm not keen ______ swimming.
44 Be loyal ______ your friends.
45 That story is new ______ me.
46 We're very proud ______ you.
47 Are you ready ______ a meal?
48 You're safe ______ danger now.
49 John is not strong ______ languages.
50 We're tired ______ this exercise.

Participial adjectives + complement

Exercise 220

Transform each of the sentences below so as to produce a subject complement consisting of a participial adjective + prepositional phrase, avoiding *by* whenever possible:

1 The young man's discomfiture amused the Countess.
2 The way she treated her servants annoyed him.
3 The young man's outburst astonished everybody.
4 Etiquette obviously did not bother him.
5 The reception they gave him did not content him.
6 His presents, however, delighted the Countess.
7 You do not disappoint me.
8 Do not let your coming adventures excite you.
9 Roger found everything around him fascinating.
10 Hunting had already interested him.
11 The Countess found his answer very pleasing.
12 His progress completely satisfied her.
13 At first, his rudeness had shocked her.
14 His conduct would have surprised his old father.
15 Now, his behaviour would not have worried his father at all.

Adjective + finite clause

Exercise 221

Combine each of the pairs of sentences below so as to produce one single sentence containing an adjective complemented by a finite clause, omitting what is in brackets:

1 You must resign. We are adamant (on that point).
2 You have made a serious error. We are afraid that (that is so).
3 Why did you behave in that way? I'm ashamed.
4 There will be a public inquiry. I am certain (of it).

5 Why do you feel so offended? We are concerned (about that).
6 You will understand. We are fully confident (of it).
7 Why do you say that? It is curious.
8 You see our point of view at last. We're delighted.
9 You must have complete trust in us. It is essential.
10 You revealed the secret. The Captain is furious.
11 You have received us so magnificently. We feel greatly honoured.
12 We are happy. You feel at home in our country.
13 You must prolong your stay. Everyone insists (on it).
14 We shall have no more travelling. That is a great relief to us.
15 You were kept waiting at the gate. I am deeply shocked.
16 My husband will not be able to attend your meeting. He is very sorry.
17 I may not be able to come with you. I'm not sure yet.
18 Did you really say that? Is it true?
19 Don't you know your programme? I'm surprised.
20 Everyone should vote on Thursday. It is vital.

Adjective + *to*-infinitive clause

Exercise 222

Indicate, by *a, b, c,* etc., to which of the following types of construction each of the sentences below could be assigned:

a He is splendid to wait.
b He is slow to react.
c He is furious to hear it.
d He is hesitant to agree.
e He is hard to convince.

1 I am very anxious to meet you.
2 We were delighted to receive your telegram.
3 You were sensible to stay indoors.
4 The clerk was prompt to answer the call.
5 This rule is easy to remember.
6 We are reluctant to leave this neighbourhood.
7 Our house is not difficult to heat.
8 Unfortunately, it isn't easy to find.
9 Are you ready to leave?
10 You would be foolish to go out in this weather.
11 John is quick to see the point.
12 He is very keen to get on.
13 We are proud to have him as a friend.
14 I was rude not to answer your letter.
15 We are happy to have you with us this evening.

Exercise 223

Rephrase each of the fifteen sentences in Exercise 222 so as to illustrate the underlying difference between the five types of construction.

Transitive complementation

Exercise 224

A direct object may be

a a noun phrase
b a noun phrase + obligatory adverbial
c a finite *that*-clause
d a finite *wh*-clause
e an infinitive clause
f a participle clause

Indicate, by *a, b, c,* etc., and with examples, which of those forms of direct object could occur after the following verbs:

ask	explain	lay	remember
believe	feel	mind	approve of
consider	gather	need	depend on
deny	hope	owe	make up
enjoy	keep	place	point out

Passive transform of monotransitive verb + direct object

Exercise 225

Give the passive transformation, if one is possible, of the following sentences, supplying the *by*-phrase only if it contains relevant and essential information:

1 Builders built this house in 1968.
2 King Khufu built the Great Pyramid.
3 The Great Pyramid contains over two million blocks of stone.
4 Each block weighs over two tons.
5 Has anyone weighed them recently?
6 People usually oppose new opinions.
7 A man with a scar across his face held my attention.
8 He hid himself behind one of the pillars.
9 Someone had admitted him by accident.
10 He must have dyed his hair.
11 His coat did not fit him properly.
12 This picture resembles the one in your drawing room.
13 I have a picture like it in my house, too.
14 Six times nine equals fifty-four.
15 No one has ever equalled your record.
16 I would like you to measure me for a suit.
17 Would this material suit you?
18 This piece of cloth measures just two metres.
19 Robert Boyle discovered the principle known as Boyle's Law.
20 The vendor has already sold this property.

Finite clause as direct object

Exercise 226

Combine each of the following pairs of sentences so as to produce one single sentence with a finite clause as object, omitting what is in brackets:

1 I have made a mistake. I admit (it).
2 Have I made a mistake? I wonder.
3 Have I given you the right figures? I doubt (it).
4 You have checked the figures carefully. I don't doubt (it).
5 You wrote me a cheque. I agree.
6 You pay me next week. I agree (to that).
7 You were going to pay me half the money today. We agreed (on that).
8 We decided (on one thing). We had gone far enough.
9 Should we continue next day or not? We could not decide.
10 How could we find the way? We had to decide (that) quickly.
11 You go ahead to get help. We have all decided (on that course of action).
12 Help will arrive at any moment. (At least), I expect (so).
13 What do you intend to do next? May I ask (that)?
14 Are we to stay here all night? May I ask (that)?
15 Please tell us the truth. All I ask is that.
16 Why not divide ourselves into two groups? (That is what) I suggest.
17 This is where we were two days ago. I remember.
18 Did we take the upper path or the lower one? Do you remember?
19 Where did we go wrong? Ah, now I know.
20 You no longer trust your leader. I sincerely regret that.

Non-finite clauses as direct object

Exercise 227

If *to talk* in *He likes to talk* is a non-finite infinitive clause, without a subject, acting as object of *likes,* give a corresponding explanation of the italicized parts of the following sentences:

a We wanted *to go home.*
b We enjoyed *walking.*
c I expected *you to be here.*
d I heard *them leave.*
e I saw *them waiting.*
f I found *my seat occupied.*

Exercise 228

Indicate, by *a, b, c,* etc., which of the finite verbs in the six sentences in Exercise 227 could be replaced by

1 ask	6 finish	11 keep	16 suggest
2 avoid	7 have	12 prefer	17 tell
3 begin	8 help	13 promise	18 threaten
4 dare	9 hope	14 refuse	19 watch
5 discover	10 imagine	15 stop	20 wish

Exercise 229

Expand the following sentences so as to clarify the difference in meaning between the two members of each pair:

1 a I remembered to fill up the form.
  b I remember filling up the form.
2 a I forgot to wake you this morning.
  b I forgot about waking you.
3 a I regret to tell you this story.
  b I regret telling you that story.
4 a I tried to turn the key another way.
  b I tried turning the key another way.
5 a My father taught me to ride.
  b He taught me riding.
6 a He had us all empty our pockets.
  b He had us all emptying our pockets.
7 a You deserve to shoot first.
  b You deserve shooting first.
8 a That boy wants to watch.
  b That boy wants watching.

Complex transitive complementation

Exercise 230

Say whether each of these sentences is (a) monotransitive or (b) complex transitive. Then put each main clause into the passive:

1 We admitted that a mistake had been made.
2 Everyone considered the mistake to be very serious.
3 We consider you to be one of our most loyal supporters.
4 We fully recognized that you have had great difficulties.
5 We find you innocent of all the charges.
6 We know your companion to be a trouble maker.
7 We have proved your story completely accurate.
8 However, we think you, at times, indiscreet.
9 We expect you to show a little more tact.
10 We regret that we must make this criticism.
11 The Air Force has reported two planes missing.
12 The authorities meant you to complete this form, and return it to the Town Hall.

Genitive before *-ing*

Exercise 231

Say which of the underlined items can be replaced by the genitive variant.

1 The police caught Wilson climbing the wall.
2 I don't approve of you climbing cliffs.
3 Do you mind me opening the window?
4 Don't let me find you opening this door again.

5 How can I stop you biting your nails?
6 I remember John telling me that story.
7 I often find myself repeating it.
8 Do you ever remember that happening to you?
9 You won't keep us waiting, will you?
10 We object to them being given preferential treatment.

-*ed* participle clauses with subject

Exercise 232

He got the watch repaired can be paraphrased as *He got someone to repair the watch.* Paraphrase the following:

1 I want this work done at once.
2 I want to see this work done properly.
3 We found the work done already.
4 I have heard this story repeated too often.
5 Can you have these notes copied before tomorrow?
6 I'm afraid we must have those trees cut down.
7 I'm afraid George has had his leg broken.
8 I think I'll have my egg fried, please.
9 Six thousand pounds was reported stolen.
10 Didn't you hear your name called?

Object complements

Exercise 233

Indicate, by *a, b, c,* etc., which of the following verbs could fill the gaps in the sentences below:

a accept
b appoint
c call
d consider
e declare
f describe
g elect
h find
i hold
j intend
k make
l mistake
m push
n put
o recognize
p regard
q take
r treat

1 They ______ John chairman.
2 They ______ John as their leader.
3 They ______ him as a true friend.
4 They ______ him reliable.
5 They ______ him very happy.
6 They ______ his appointment to be permanent.
7 We ______ the door open.
8 We ______ your room for the library.
9 We ______ the pole straight.
10 We ______ the incident closed.

Exercise 234

Indicate, by *a, b, c,* etc., which of the 18 verbs in Exercise 233 could fill the gaps in the following:

1 John was ______ chairman.
2 John was ______ (chairman).
3 He was ______ as reliable.
4 Your room was ______ for the library.
5 The incident was ______ closed.

Exercise 235

a Move the object complement, if it is mobile.
b Replace the object by the corresponding pronoun, then write out the new sentence:

1 George's conduct made Mary very angry.
2 He had broken open her wardrobe.
3 Let us set free all the prisoners.
4 Will this agreement make the end of all the fighting possible?
5 Can you have ready for tomorrow the minutes of our last two meetings?
6 I would like you to leave clear those two cupboards over by the window.
7 We shall not appoint officers of the society those members who do not attend regularly.

Ditransitive complementation

Exercise 236

Rephrase each of the following sentences using the pattern

(Subject) + verb + direct object + prepositional phrase,

but only when such rephrasing is admissible:

1 The townsfolk accorded us a warm welcome.
2 I have asked you a great favour.
3 We booked you a double room with bath.
4 Bring me your essay this afternoon.
5 Someone has brought us some grapes.
6 Call me a taxi right away.
7 Can anyone cash me a cheque?
8 We have caused you so much trouble.
9 This suit only cost me forty dollars.
10 These pills haven't done me much good.
11 I will give you all the necessary information.
12 Someone has just handed me this message.
13 I'll leave you your dinner in the oven.
14 An uncle left her a small fortune.
15 Do we owe the milkman anything?
16 I have paid George the whole sum.
17 You must show me your ticket.
18 I have told you the truth.

19 Throw me that towel, will you?
20 I wish you good luck.

Exercise 237

a Read the 20 sentences in Exercise 236, omitting the indirect object whenever such omission can be made without detriment to the sense.
b In which of those 20 sentences could the direct object be ellipted?

Exercise 238

Give two different passive transformations for the following sentences in Exercise 236: 2, 3, 8, 11, 12, 14, 16, 17, 18.

Exercise 239

a Supply the missing prepositions.
b Read the sentence, ellipting the prepositional phrase where possible.
c Give the passive transformation of the whole original sentence.
d Form a question for each sentence, on the following model:
What example can this one be compared with?

1 They accused Barlow ______ a certain crime.
2 People admired Asquith ______ certain qualities.
3 We have assigned you ______ a particular task.
4 Everyone blames you ______ a certain mistake.
5 Everyone blames the mistake ______ somebody.
6 The police charged Manson ______ the murder.
7 We can compare this writer ______ a well-known novelist.
8 I am confining you ______ certain limits.
9 They congratulated Henry ______ his medal.
10 They will consult us ______ the plan.
11 We have credited you ______ a fixed amount.
12 The guards deprived the visitors ______ certain weapons.
13 This card entitled us ______ certain privileges.
14 I shall exempt them ______ certain duties.
15 We have freed you ______ a great anxiety.
16 We have already informed them ______ the decision.
17 The treasurer has invested our money ______ stocks.
18 I have only mentioned this matter ______ one of the professors.
19 They have provided blankets ______ some of the refugees.
20 They have provided some of the refugees ______ blankets.
21 We have supplied food ______ certain families.
22 We have supplied those families ______ food.
23 I am thanking you ______ your kindness.

Exercise 240

a Supply the missing verbs. Then,
b put each sentence into the passive, as follows:
We took care of it ~ It was taken care of.

1 You must not ______ sight of your main objective.
2 I don't like people ______ fun of me.
3 It is time you ______ a stop to this nonsense.
4 The raiders ______ fire to three haystacks.
5 We have not ______ pace with the latest research.

Exercise 241

a Supply the missing verbs. Then,
b put each sentence into the passive in two different ways:

1 Have you ______ proper care of this equipment?
2 I hope you will not ______ advantage of my absence.
3 We have ______ good use of the laboratory.
4 We have ______ careful note of your complaint.
5 The students have ______ no notice of these instructions.

Exercise 242

Indicate, by *a, b* or *c,* into which of the following three sentences the verbs below could fit:

a John said that there would be trouble.
b John told me that there would be trouble.
c John explained to me that he had been ill.

1 admit	5 convince	9 mention	13 remark	17 state
2 announce	6 declare	10 persuade	14 remind	18 suggest
3 assure	7 explain	11 point out	15 report	19 tell
4 confess	8 inform	12 promise	16 say	20 warn

Exercise 243

Rephrase the sentences below, where possible, by using the pattern:
I persuaded John to see a doctor.

1 I persuaded John that he should see a doctor.
2 I persuaded him that his wife should take a holiday.
3 I convinced him that he should be more careful.
4 I advised him that he should stay in bed.
5 I warned him that he should not go out.
6 I assured him that he would get pneumonia.
7 I reminded him that he should take his medicine.
8 I reminded him that he had been overworking.
9 I requested him that he should keep me informed of his condition.
10 I assured him that he would have proper care.

Exercise 244

Note the following two-fold analysis:

A	He wanted	Mary to teach Bob.
	He wanted	Mary to.
B	He persuaded Mary	to teach Bob.
	He persuaded Mary	(to)

In which of those two ways could the following sentences be analysed?

1 I would love Mary to teach me.
2 I would hate Joan to drive my car.
3 I advise you to be more careful.
4 May I invite you to join us?
5 We expect you to be here by eight.
6 I beseech you to come to our aid.
7 We wish you to help us.
8 Can you help us to regain our liberty?
9 We would allow you to live here for ever.
10 We beg you not to leave us.

13 The complex noun phrase

Noun modifiers

Exercise 245

Say which of the underlined noun modifiers are (a) restrictive, (b) non-restrictive:

1 My poor old mother suffers from arthritis.
2 Her devoted elder daughter takes care of her.
3 Where did you get that beautiful carpet in the hall?
4 George was wearing a sports shirt, light cotton slacks and open-toed sandals.
5 I often see men who went to school with me.
6 The great fire of 1666 started in the house of a baker.
7 Oh, you sensible man. Good old Henry.
8 An old proverb says: Ill news travels apace.
9 Cuzco is still a thriving city, its Inca buildings merged into the buildings of the Spaniard.
10 A queue of long-haired, strangely dressed youths formed up outside our stately theatre.
11 The man who called here last night must have been Jeremy Taylor.
12 Jeremy Taylor, who called here last night, left this message for you.
13 The theatre to which we were taken was the oldest one in Paris.
14 The theatre, to which we were taken every week, was a great delight to us.
15 All these articles, which have been given to us by well-wishers, are to be sold to raise money for the club.
16 All the articles you see here have been sold.
17 The students whose names are below the line on this list must sit the examination again.
18 The demonstrators, whose names had already been taken by the police, refused to move.
19 Roses do very well in my garden, which is a perfect paradise in June.
20 Many things grow in my garden which I never planted in it.

Explicitness in modifiers

Exercise 246

Make the postmodifier in each of these sentences more explicit by replacing it (a) by two different participle clauses, then (b) by two different relative clauses:

1 Do you know the man with the overcoat?
2 I don't recognize the man in the garden.
3 The President will only shake hands with the people in the front row.
4 Children at school will have first priority.
5 This book by Hertford will give you all the facts.
6 The new house was built with money from wealthy landowners.

Unambiguous use of postmodifiers

Exercise 247

Explain the absurdity of the sentences below in terms of noun phrase modifiers and adverbial adjuncts. Then rephrase each sentence.

1 I have discussed the question of stocking the new pig farm with my staff.
2 Look at that silver cup which my daughter won for dancing on the mantel-piece.
3 I have to give a lecture on the disposal of industrial waste to students of engineering.
4 Last week an eighteenth century chair was bought by a dealer with beautifully carved legs for only forty pounds.
5 You can buy a copy of this book on breast-feeding at your local bookstore.
6 There are so many different washing machines on the market that you would be well advised to consult an expert on the make.
7 A radish has been grown by one of our members the size of a turnip.
8 There is more to Ambridge than the mask of the bizarre behind which our old-world village tries to hide.

Relative clauses

Exercise 248

Replace the relative pronoun *that* by *who, whom, which* or zero:

1 This is the house that Jack built.
2 He looks like a dog that has lost its tail.
3 Danny, our dog that followed us all the way from Scotland, has just died.
4 Don't believe everything that you read in the newspapers.
5 Babies that were born prematurely had little chance of survival.
6 Children that disobey their parents should be punished.
7 Murray was the sole survivor from a famous ship that sank on her first voyage.
8 Murray was the only person that survived the disaster.

9 The party that was responsible for this extraordinary piece of legislation is now out of office.
10 The party that were responsible are now trying to repair the damage.

Exercise 249

The sentence *There is the officer to whom I spoke* can have four variations, viz:

a There is the officer whom I spoke to.
b ,, ,, ,, ,, who I spoke to
c ,, ,, ,, ,, that I spoke to.
d ,, ,, ,, ,, I spoke to.

Give as many variations of that kind as possible for the following:

1 Here is the article about which I was speaking.
2 Here is a book which will tell you all about it.
3 Is this the book from which that quotation was taken?
4 Is Thompson the man to whom you were referring?
5 He is a man for whom I have the greatest respect.
6 Is this really the house in which Shakespeare was born?
7 That was the very day on which I first saw Mary.
8 I shall always remember the way in which you received us that evening.
9 It was a century during which the country suffered continually from wars.
10 This is a matter concerning which you would be well advised to consult a lawyer.

Non-restrictive and sentential relative clauses

Exercise 250

Identify the antecedent of the following relative clauses:

1 We were taken every week to the theatre, at which new plays were constantly being produced.
2 We were taken every week to the theatre, which was a great delight to us.
3 We went to the theatre every week, which was our one relaxation.
4 The singer gave five encores, for which he received enthusiastic applause.
5 He gave five encores, all of which were quite new to the audience.
6 He gave five encores, which was a very generous acknowledgement of the welcome he had received.
7 The climbers spent two nights on the mountainside, which was swept by biting winds.
8 They spent two nights on the mountainside, which was an ordeal for the hardiest of them.
9 We test every bottle of Buzz in our laboratories, which is why it is so reliable.
10 We apply a laboratory test to every bottle of Buzz, which is then hygienically corked.

Appositive clauses

Exercise 251

Rephrase each of the sentences below, using a factive abstract noun + appositive clause. Say whether the clause so formed is (a) restrictive or (b) non-restrictive:

1 It is still believed in some countries that the earth is flat.
2 It is true that the earth is round, and that has been evident to every astronaut.
3 Columbus assumed that the land he had discovered was the eastern extremity of Asia, but this was soon proved wrong.
4 Columbus reported that there was a king in the south who owned great quantities of gold, and this lured many explorers to the search for El Dorado.
5 People suspect that smoking has something to do with cancer: this rests on several kinds of evidence.
6 When scientists argued that cigarette smoking may increase one's chances of developing cancer of the lung, this was not well received in certain quarters.
7 You may have gone to sleep during my lecture but that does not exempt you from writing this essay.
8 You went to sleep during the lecture, and this fact suggests that you should go to bed earlier.
9 You excuse yourself by saying people keep asking you out, but I cannot accept that.
10 I know that I can always call upon you for support, and that is a great comfort to me.

Postmodification by non-finite clauses

Exercise 252

Convert the participle clause into a relative clause in each of these sentences:

1 At the station, we were met by a man carrying a copy of *The Times*.
2 He was accompanied by a porter weighing at least 150 kilos.
3 A car, coming unexpectedly out of a side street, crashed into us.
4 We collided with a car driven by a young man without a licence.
5 Any driver not having a licence ought to be sent to jail right away.
6 The train standing at platform six is for Brussels and Ostend.
7 Any article left in this bus was taken at once to the Lost Property Office.
8 Any dutiable articles not declared to the Customs will be liable to confiscation.
9 Presents costing less than ten pounds in all may be imported duty free.
10 Anyone not hearing that noise must have been stone deaf.
11 Everybody, hearing the noise, jumped up in alarm.
12 The castle, burnt down in the sixteenth century, was never rebuilt.

Exercise 253

Convert the infinitive clause in each of these sentences into a relative clause:

1 The next train to arrive is from Edinburgh.
2 The first man to fly non-stop across the Atlantic was John Alcock.
3 Was Cortes the first European ever to see the Pacific Ocean?
4 The best man to see for your eye trouble is the Professor of Ophthalmology.
5 The man for John to speak to first is the Director of the Museum.
6 The cheapest place to eat at is the cafeteria.
7 You'll find the best time to get there is just after twelve.
8 The way to get to the head of the queue is to slip in through the kitchen.
9 Will you buy me a magazine to read on the journey?
10 Here is something for you to do while you're waiting.
11 The only thing left to consider now is how to get away without being seen.
12 The last problem, to be considered at our next meeting, is how to invest the money.

Exercise 254

Rewrite these sentences, using a noun phrase with infinitive clause as post-modifier.

1 We planned to cross the river at night but failed.
2 Our appeal for volunteers for another attempt was greeted with enthusiasm.
3 We thought the idea that we should create a diversion upstream was a good one.
4 We did not wish to waste lives in another frontal attack.
5 Our allies promised to send reinforcements but did not do so.
6 We felt they were cowardly to hesitate to come to our aid.
7 It was disgraceful that they should refuse to fulfil their promise.
8 This only made us more determined to succeed on our own.
9 Meanwhile, we were not disturbed when the enemy threatened to attack us.
10 Nor were we deceived when they proposed that we should call a truce.

Postmodification by prepositional phrases

Exercise 255

Replace each prepositional phrase by a relative clause that will make the meaning of the postmodification more explicit:

1 A house by the church.
2 A picture by a famous artist.
3 The plane for Moscow.
4 Warm clothes for Moscow.
5 A land for all seasons.
6 The man for the job.
7 The man with your wife.
8 The man with a gun.
9 The man without a hat.
10 A student from Portugal.
11 A quotation from Shakespeare.
12 Instructions in case of fire.
13 The pleasure of your company.
14 A man of strong will.

15 A man of property.
16 A man of my acquaintance.
17 The flint wall of our cellar.
18 The people of Asia.
19 The rule of the majority.
20 A Jack of all trades.

Premodification by participles

Exercise 256

'Everything here depends on the potentiality of the participle to indicate a permanent or characteristic feature.'

Accepting that as a criterion, paraphrase the items underlined in the sentences below:

1 The Commander was pacing the quarter-deck with the navigating officer.
2 I read Edgar Allan Poe's tales with a sort of shackled fascination.
3 I learned to climb the tree with a kind of absent-minded dexterity.
4 The paid servants had their specified position in the household.
5 The roses grew in great perfumed masses all over the garden.
6 I took a couple of furnished rooms in Vincent Square.
7 The French tutor was a charming young lady.
8 The outstanding discovery of sunspot activity was made by a German chemist.
9 He concluded that sunspots vary in a fairly well-defined cycle of about eleven years.
10 Hong Kong is a mainly Cantonese-speaking city.
11 This writer makes his point with terrifying emphasis.
12 Sheila is the adopted daughter of a well-known banker.
13 You have a standing invitation to come with us at any time.
14 The Chief felt thoroughly lost in the crowded streets of London.
15 A surprising factor has been the political energy of the Swiss.

Exercise 257

The sentence *This book interests people very much* can be rephrased:

This is a very interesting book

Indicate by *Yes* whether each of the sentences below can be rephrased with the participle as premodifier, and add *v* if the participle can be modified by *very*:

1 This news has alarmed me very much.
2 George is a man who amuses me.
3 These people are very amused.
4 That story is most astonishing.
5 Those children behave themselves.
6 Those children behave themselves well.
7 Those students seem very bored.
8 There are many faces in the room that look bored.
9 That candle is burning.

10 That man is always drinking.
11 This report encourages us.
12 This is an agreement that will last.
13 We have a supply of fuel but it is limited.
14 Those seats are reserved.
15 Those clients were very satisfied.
16 That man seems surprised.
17 This result is totally unexpected.
18 These circumstances worry me.

Exercise 258
Explain the difference in function between the two words underlined in each of the following pairs of sentences:

1 a Mary and John were married quietly last year.
  b They were married when I first met them.
2 a Mary is charming.
  b The snake-charmer is charming a cobra.
3 a That story is interesting.
  b The speaker is certainly interesting his audience.
4 a The man painting that picture is a real artist.
  b He is painting it extremely well.
5 a You are embarrassing the ladies.
  b Your stories are embarrassing.
6 a John is promising you too much.
  b Nevertheless, he is a promising young man.

Exercise 259
Change the form of the phrases below so that the postmodifiers become premodifiers:

1 A house that has been built well.
2 The article which was mentioned above.
3 An improvement that is needed badly.
4 A secret that has been kept closely.
5 Wealth that has never been told.
6 Cruelty such as we have never heard of before.
7 Central heating fired by oil.
8 Girls with blue eyes.
9 A man with a red nose.
10 A censor with a heavy hand.
11 A tiger with teeth like sabres.
12 A boat with a flat bottom.

Premodification by nouns

Exercise 260

Convert each of the phrases below by using the pattern *head+postmodifying phrase,* thus:

The cupboard door ~ The door of the cupboard.

1 water supply
2 a motor-bus service
3 repair personnel
4 the life sciences
5 fish protein production
6 a space probe
7 a radio signal
8 a power station
9 peak power
10 price rise rate
11 graphite blocks
12 ground-water possibilities
13 surface hydrology
14 storage capacity
15 the dam foundation
16 a diversion canal
17 landing-gear components
18 the impact strength (of steel)
19 the volume change
20 accident prevention legislation

Multiple premodification

Exercise 261

Expand the following phrases so as to make it clear what words are being modified by what:

1 a short, red-haired man
2 a short-haired fox terrier
3 a small, sparsely-furnished office
4 a totally committed, self-effacing man
5 pretty good entertainment expenses
6 two attractive flat-roofed villas
7 attractive two-bedroomed apartments
8 elegant period town houses
9 school careers adviser
10 new, reasonably-priced leather jackets

Relative sequence of premodifiers

Exercise 262

From each of the following sets of data, form one phrase composed entirely of premodifiers + head word:

1 two chairs; made of oak; beautifully-carved
2 your blue, old, scarf; the silk one that you bought in Japan
3 this pot—round, small, made of iron, used for cooking
4 the murder that took place in the villa by the side of the river
5 their masks to keep out the smog; neat, white
6 stamps for insurance, several thousand, unused, stolen recently

7 all these shells, walnut shells, shrivelled, broken
8 a famous school, teaching medicine, in Scotland
9 the cultivator that sells best in the country
10 a cottage in the country, very picturesque though crumbling slightly; roof of thatch

14 Focus, theme and emphasis

Information focus

Exercise 263

Read the following passage; then read the answers to the questions below, placing nuclear stress on the appropriate word or syllable:

> 'It is now forty years since I went up to Oxford. The world then was a more leisurely place than it is now, and Oxford was a much more leisurely place. From the point of view of an irreverent undergraduate, the dons of that time belonged to one or other of three quite separate classes: there were figures of fun; there were men who were technically competent but uninteresting; and there was a small class of men whom we admired whole-heartedly.'

1 Which university did the writer of that passage go to?
He went to the University of Oxford.

2 Was he at school at Oxford?
No, he was at the university there.

3 Did he live in Oxford or outside it?
He lived in Oxford.

4 How long ago was that? Thirty years ago?
It was forty years ago.

5 What was the world like in those days?
It was a more leisurely place than it is now.

6 Was Oxford more leisurely too?
Yes, it was much more leisurely.

7 When the writer mentions three separate classes, to whom is he referring?
He is referring to the dons.

8 Did the undergraduates find the technically competent dons interesting?
No, they found them uninteresting.

9 Did the undergraduates admire the third class of men?
Yes, they admired them whole-heartedly.

10 Does the writer speak about going up to Oxford or going down to it?
He says he went up to Oxford.

Focus on the operator

Exercise 264

Read lines A below silently. Then read lines B aloud, with the appropriate emphasis:

1 A I don't think you're really interested in this.
  B But I am interested.
2 A You haven't understood what I've been saying.
  B Excuse me, but I have understood.
3 A I don't think you see the point.
  B I do, honestly. I do see the point.
4 A You always thought I was wrong.
  B That's untrue. I never did think you were wrong.
5 A Is this the right road?
  B I'm not sure, but it might be.
6 A Well, is this the right road?
  B Yes, that must be it.
7 A We have surely come the longest way round.
  B Yes, indeed, we must have done.
8 A I think we've taken the wrong turning again.
  B Surely not. We can't have done.
9 A We're not here yet.
  B We are. That's the house. We are here.
10 A Have you parked the car properly?
  B Not yet, but I will in a minute.

Exercise 265

In answering the questions below, use (a) the information given in brackets, and (b) the passive voice as a means of achieving end-focus.

1 Who invented the telephone? (Graham Bell, in 1876)
2 Were Christopher Columbus and his men the first Europeans to discover America? (Norsemen landed on the coast of North America in the 10th or 11th century)
3 What is the cause of influenza? (Two main types of virus cause it)
4 Why is it comparatively easy to eat Chinese food with chopsticks? (Chinese cooks first cut up all their ingredients very small)
5 Where does ultra-violet light come from? (The sun emits it)
6 In the Middle Ages, how did workmen manage for board and lodging? (The master for whom they worked provided them with board and lodging)

Theme

Exercise 266

Identify (a) the subject, and (b) the theme, of each of the sentences below. Say whether the theme occurs as S, Cs, Od, Co, C prep (prepositional complement), P (predication) or V (verb):

1 My husband will carry your suitcase.
2 But that heavy trunk he can't take.
3 Not one girl in ten can a young man trust these days.
4 A scandal I call it.
5 An angel that's what you are, my dear.
6 That shelf, he probably put it on.
7 Fool Joe may be, but thief he is not.
8 Break his bloody neck, I will.
9 Die is the last thing I shall do, doctor.
10 Suddenly, there was a loud knock at the door.

Inversion
Exercise 267
Rearrange each of the sentences below, using accepted patterns of subject-verb inversion:

1 The rain fell down.
2 The prices went up and up.
3 He was so anxious to turn over a new leaf that he actually changed his name.
4 He would not give up writing his satires under any circumstances.
5 His determination to tell the truth about his experiences was just as firm.
6 It has never been more difficult for a writer to make his name.
7 A tall, gaunt figure stood at the far end of the room, staring at us.
8 We only then realized how much he had suffered.
9 His Majesty the Emperor is now mounting the steps.
10 You would witness a spectacle like this in no other country in the world.

Cleft sentences
Exercise 268
From each of the sentences below form cleft sentences that will focus, in turn, on the different elements given in brackets:

1 Sartoris first saw an enormous serpent approaching (S, Od).
2 Captain Mackay reported this incident to Admiral Gage (S, Od, C prep).
3 He sent Admiral Gage a report of this incident (Oi).
4 The *Daedalus* docked at Bristol on a dark and cloudy afternoon in 1896 (Complement of *at*, complement of *on*).
5 Joyce Cary's first novel was called *Aissa Saved* (Joyce Cary's, first, *Aissa Saved*).
6 The book took a long time to write because it raised so many difficult questions (*because*-clause).

7 Somerset Maugham gave up medicine after his first novel had been accepted for publication (*after*-clause).
8 Schwabe only felt justified in publishing his conclusions after eighteen years of continuous research (*only after eighteen years* etc.).
9 The dominant constraint on broadcasting is the restriction on ether-space (Cs).
10 The most striking feature of malaria in Tropical Africa is its high endemicity with hardly any seasonal changes. (Cs).

Exercise 269
Using the material in Exercise 268, form sentences beginning as follows:

1 The sailors believed it was an enormous serpent . . .
2 It would have been to Admiral Gage . . .
3 It must have been Admiral Gage . . .
4 It was probably Bristol . . .
5 I think it was Cary's first novel . . .
6 What he saw approaching was . . .
7 What Captain Mackay did was to . . .
8 The author who gave up medicine after . . .
9 Somerset Maugham was the author . . .
10 Tropical Africa is where . . .

Anticipatory *it*
Exercise 270
Rewrite the following sentences beginning each with anticipatory *it*:

1 This question is very easy to answer.
2 Finlay is a difficult man to understand.
3 He is impossible to do business with.
4 He is quite likely to let you down.
5 He is known to double-cross his best friends.
6 You seem to have taken a dislike to him.
7 Yes, I happen to have had some nasty experiences in dealing with him.
8 He is said to have been in prison once already.
9 You appear to know all about his past life.
10 He is certain to be charged with an offence.

Existential *there*
Exercise 271
Rephrase these sentences so as to begin each with existential *there*:

1 A small, grey monkey was wearing my best silk tie.
2 Monkeys were under the table, swinging on light-fittings, everywhere.
3 A boy named George Sampeter sat in the same class as me.

4 Several trains were coming into the station at the same time.
5 During the Great Fire, things called firesquirts were used in an attempt to quench the flames.
6 Many citizens believed that the fire had been caused by foreigners.
7 My front door had a bolt but I never used it.
8 The Maldives consist of several thousand little islands.
9 People believed that an ancient city lay somewhere in the mountains.
10 Beneath our house was an old cellar with a thick flint wall.

Exercise 272
Rephrase these sentences using existential *there*:

1 We should have a stronger light on the staircase.
2 I am sure that a mistake has been made.
3 We do not want any disturbance to occur.
4 Having a bus stop so near the house is a great advantage.
5 Having no further business, the Chairman closed the meeting.
6 An impregnable castle stood on the top of the hill.
7 A time will come when you look back on this day with pride.
8 Is anyone waiting to see me?
9 We won't have any difficulty, will we?
10 No messages have come for me, have they?

Existential *have*
Exercise 273
Rephrase these sentences using existential *have*:

1 I think there is some dust in my eye.
2 There is mud all over your coat.
3 A friend of my father's is in the Ministry.
4 I wish to raise two questions at the meeting this afternoon.
5 There is something important that I want to tell you.

Extraposition
Exercise 274
Rephrase the following sentences using the anticipatory *it*:

1 To be with you here this evening is a great pleasure.
2 You were so kind to invite us.
3 To spoil this fine drawing would be a pity.
4 What you say does not matter in the least.
5 How he came to have such a valuable painting is a mystery.
6 I think a good idea would be to get up a petition.
7 That you should feel obliged to resign at this point is regretted.

8 Seeing you sitting all alone makes me feel sad.
9 Getting the car on the boat was rather complicated.
10 Do you find living here very dull?
11 I cannot possibly forgive him.
12 What must be done is something which we leave you to decide.

Discontinuous noun phrases

Exercise 275

Rephrase the following, postponing all or part of the postmodifier in the long noun phrase, but avoiding ambiguity:

1 That loaf that you sold me was stale.
2 The time to face the facts squarely has now come.
3 A public inquiry to investigate the causes of the disaster was instituted immediately.
4 The belief that foreigners are responsible for all our economic troubles is commonly held.
5 A list of all the museums in Rome will be sent to you.
6 A great deal of nonsense about the modern permissive society is published in the press.
7 Stories of how people have lived for several weeks without food are sometimes told.
8 A report on meals served to children in schools has just been issued.
9 The question of how to allocate these funds most fairly will arise.
10 New evidence in support of the existence of an ancient city on Santorini has recently been published.

Appendix I Word-formation

Prefixation

Exercise 276

Give three examples, other than those in the *University Grammar of English*, for each of the following:

a the negative prefixes: *un-, non-, in-, dis-* and *a-*;
b the reversative prefixes: *un-, de-* and *dis-*;
c the pejorative prefixes: *mis-, mal-* and *pseudo-*;
d the prefixes of degree or size: *arch-, super-, out-, sur-, sub-, over-, under-, hyper-, ultra-* and *mini-*;
e the prefixes of attitude: *co-, counter-, anti-, pro-*;
f the locative prefixes: *super-, sub-, inter-, trans-*;
g the prefixes of time and order: *fore-, pre-, post-, ex-* and *re-*;
h number prefixes: *uni-, mono-, bi-, di-, tri-, multi-, poly-;*
i other prefixes: *auto-, neo-, pan-, proto-, semi-, vice-*;
j conversion prefixes: *be-, en-* and *a-*.

Suffixation

Exercise 277

Give three examples, other than those given in the *Grammar*, for each of the following:

1 *Noun → noun suffixes*
a Occupational   b Diminutive   c Feminine
d Status   e Others

2 *Noun → adjective suffixes*
a *-al*   b *-ese*   c *-ful*   d *-ian*   m *-y*
e *-ic*   f *-ish*   g *-ist*   h *-ite*
i *-ive*   j *-less*   k *-ly*   l *-ous*

3 *Other adjective suffixes*
a *-able*   b *-ible*   c *-ed*

4 *Verb → noun suffixes*
a *-age*   b *-al*   c *-ant*   d *-ee*
e *-er*   f *-ing*   g *-or*   h *-ment*

5 *Adjective → noun suffixes*
a *-ity*   b *-ness*

6 *Verb suffixes*
a *-en* b *-ify* c *-ise* or *-ize*
7 *Adverb suffixes*
a *-ly* b *-ward(s)* c *-wise*

Conversion
Exercise 278
Using the *Grammar* as a guide, draw up a scheme of classification for conversion as a derivational process. Then fit the following words into it:

ache	boast	cork	face	jump
address	bone	corner	fall	kick
advance	bottle	cost	fan	kill
aim	box	cover	fancy	knot
amount	brain	crack	feast	laugh
answer	bribe	crowd	film	list
arm	brown	curve	fire	mail
arrest	cage	date	flavour	mass
aside	can	decay	fool	motive
attack	captain	delight	form	must
attempt	catch	demand	fright	nail
average	centre	desire	glass	narrow
away	chair	despair	group	near
back	charm	dirty	guess	net
bag	cheer	doubt	handle	pale
bank	class	dream	head	paste
bath	clean	dust	honour	people
beard	coat	empty	humble	piece
better	colour	end	inch	plan
blind	control	escape	joke	plough

Shift of stress
Exercise 279
Form sentences to illustrate the use of the words below as both nouns and verbs. Then read aloud each of the sentences you have formed:

abstract	conflict	decrease	escort	insult	rebel
accent	conscript	desert	essay	object	record
addict	content	detail	exploit	perfume	retail
ally	contest	dictate	export	permit	subject
attribute	contract	digest	extract	present	survey
combine	contrast	discount	import	produce	suspect
compress	converse	discourse	impress	progress	torment
concert	convert	entrance	incense	prospect	transfer
conduct	convict	envelope	increase	protest	transport

Compounding

Exercise 280

Using the *Grammar* as a guide, draw up a scheme for the classification of compounds in English, using the following as examples:

birdcage
blackboard
bloodstain
bluebell
brainwash
breathtaking
brick red
bus driver
day-dream
dragonfly
dressmaking
eating apple
everlasting
facecloth
factory-worker
fathead
frying pan
gamekeeper
glowworm
haircut
handmade
handwriting
headache
homework
hothouse
housekeeper
motorcycle
new-born
ocean-going
power plant
raindrop
rainfall
safety belt
scarecrow
self-service
silkworm
sleepwalking
springboard
spring-clean
steam engine
sun-bathing
tax-free
telephone call
theatre-goer
toothpaste
treadmill
washing-machine
watchdog
working party
writing desk

Appendix II Stress, rhythm and intonation

Word stress

Exercise 281

Mark the main and secondary stresses in all of the words below, using the following method:

conˈservative ˌconserˈvation ˈco-ˌpilot

1 admire, admirable, admiration
2 bureau, bureaucracy, bureaucratic
3 converse (noun), converse (verb), conversation
4 decay, decadent, de-centralize
5 electric, electricity, electrification
6 final, finale, finality, finance
7 govern, government, governmental
8 homogeneous, homogeneousness, homogeneity
9 inflame, inflammable, inflammation
10 justify, justifiable, justification
11 library, librarian, laboratory
12 multiply, multiplicity, multiplication
13 neglect, neglectfulness, negligible
14 operate, operation, operative
15 prepare, preparatory, preparation
16 prepare, pre-judge, propose, pro-rector
17 qualify, qualification, quality, qualitative
18 restore, restorative, restoration, re-paint
19 science, scientist, scientific, scientifically
20 transport (noun), transport (verb), transportable, transportation
21 union, unite, unity, unify, unification
22 understand, undo, unnecessary, untie
23 vital, vitality, vitriol, vitriolic
24 gold watch, gold mine; cement works, cement wall; toy factory
25 boiling water, boiling point; a running stream, a running shoe; a changing room, changing circumstances

Rhythm and intonation

Exercise 282

Mark the stressed syllables in the sentences below, assuming they are spoken with normal stress and rhythm. Mark nuclear stress with falling intonation, pattern as follows: with falling intonation, *conCLÙsion*; with rising intonation, *reSÚLTS*.

1 Thinking about it led us to an interesting conclusion.
2 The process of changing a computer program can be compared with human dreams.
3 These bookshelves are becoming very popular in Sweden. We have recently added an extra unit to them.
4 Can you tell me when we shall see the results?
5 May I call you a taxi or something?
6 You aren't looking in the right direction, I think.
7 I never imagined that such a thing could happen. Did you?
8 They'll be issuing some new tickets tomorrow.
9 Ferguson saw the fire, and Parkinson saw it too.
10 Are you certain that this is the right road?
11 How many people were killed in street accidents last year?
12 None of us have finished Chapter Two yet.
13 Some of the others have finished it already.
14 I have a problem that is much more complicated than that.
15 What I would like to do is to go somewhere really quiet.
16 I am not aware that I gave you permission to leave.
17 That is all I have to tell you, Mrs Ferguson.
18 What he was doing with that gun I can't imagine.
19 What was he doing with that gun, I wonder?
20 Are there any messages for me, I wonder?

Appendix III Punctuation

Exercise 283
Punctuate the following:

1 The monkeys were under the table perching on chairs swinging on light-fittings
2 I know the answer he said you need a Pied Piper
3 Leaving us at the gate they disappeared into the house
4 Leaving us at the gate like that was rather discourteous
5 Stanley its been a long time since we met hasnt it
6 Robert Burns Scotlands national poet was born in 1759
7 The poet Robert Burns was born at Alloway Ayrshire
8 The theatre to which we were taken was the oldest one in Paris
9 The theatre to which we went every week was a great delight to us
10 A lawyer by training when forced by events to be a soldier he proved himself a great soldier
11 Whatever he had to do he did well naturally
12 Whatever he had to do with it he was not the ringleader
13 Thirteen thousand houses nearly one hundred churches St Pauls Cathedral the Royal Exchange even Guildhall itself went up in flames
14 In the end they had to resort to gunpowder blowing up whole rows of houses and that stopped the fire that and the fact that the wind died down
15 For most of my life childhood boyhood and more we lived in the country
16 The lawn almost the only uncontaminated place in that ancient neighbourhood had hitherto been innocent of any dark secret
17 The Manager of the Court Theatre put on a play that failed the next play he had arranged to put on was not ready and he was at his wits end he read a play of mine called *Lady Frederick* and though he did not much like it he thought it might just run for the six weeks till the play he had in mind to follow it with could be produced
18 Presently the German tutor was aroused the cordial and intelligent Herr Steinweg who explained I had not been expected so soon he showed me my room also my bed but I could not occupy the latter because the outgoing English tutor Bristow had not yet vacated it

19 He wants independence he wants colour in his life he dreams of achievements none of which seems possible in the village his reading and he is an avid reader seems hardly relevant to his actual life

20 An image in some way resembles the thing it stands for whereas a symbol is not like it but represents it arbitrarily works of art are images and a work of art is an image of feeling of course a work of art is not an image of feeling only because we normally do not experience feelings by themselves we feel towards or about things or people or ideas so that a work of art if it is to transmit feelings must also represent the object towards which the feelings are directed

Suggested answers

Note: Other answers than those given in the following pages may well be acceptable. If it is a question of what is stated or implied in *A University Grammar of English,* then the *Grammar* itself is the obvious authority on whether an answer is acceptable or not. If it is a question of modern English grammatical usage, then the actual usage of a considerable number of educated native-speakers of English can be used as a criterion. If the user of this Workbook is in doubt as to what would be a correct answer to one of the questions in it, then these suggestions are offered for his guidance.

Ex. 1 *1.* a. British *or* American *or* Scottish *or* Canadian; b. regional. *2.* a. equally related; b. superior *or* inferior; *3.* a. phonology; b. grammar. *4.* a. uneducated *or* educated; b. dialectal. *5.* a. educated speech; b. adopted. *6.* a. no; b. but; c. uniformity; d. spelling; e. divergence; f. grammar; g. vocabulary. *7.* a. less; b. medium; c. lacks; d. and *or* but; e. more. *8.* a. approach *or* attitude; b. what; *9.* a. interference; b. a new dialect *or* another variety. *10.* a. generally; b. adopted *or* recognized; c. private; d. educational; e. public; f. schools. *11.* a. standard; b. register; c. medium; d. formal. *12.* a. We have gotten; b. American; c. autumn; d. British.

Ex. 2 *1.* a. Centre (Brit.); b. been in correspondence, Messrs, concerning (official, or commercial); d. 'I have' rather than 'I've' (formal); *2.* b. incomplete second sentence (advertising) d. we've, give it a try (informal). *3.* a. railway (Brit.); c. the appeal to 'sir' and 'Dick' suggests spoken; d. don't (informal); e. don't know nothing, we was, was we (substandard); *4.* a. tap (Brit.); b. & c. use of imperatives, and absence of definite article before nouns and of a pronoun after 'leave', are typical of technical, written instructions. *5.* b. & c. hereinafter, this my Will, the incidence of such remuneration, as set forth therein (legal, written). *6.* c. & d. the -m-, indicating hesitation, and the disjointed sentence, suggest a written transcription of unprepared speech. *7.* c. & d. the expression 'I feel pretty sure' in a well-formed sentence suggests informal English prepared, in writing, to be spoken. *8.* a. labeled (Am.); b. 3·9 millicuries of Cl-labeled DDT, inert granules, 0·2 pounds DDT per acre (scientific); c. 0·2 pounds DDT per acre (written); d. features already mentioned (formal). *9.* b. & c. imperatives and absence of articles and pronouns (technical instructions, cooking recipe, written). *10.* c. & d. we are, we read many books, we cannot, whom, and the well-constructed sentence, are evidence of written, formal, literary English. *11.* a. Sure, Shucks (Am.); c. & d. well-formed sentences, combined with 'I guess I've eaten' and 'I don't know', suggest an attempt to represent informal speech in writing. *12.* b., c. & d. was reported missing, believed to have crashed (journalistic, written, formal).

Ex. 3 Examples: *1.* I have recently been; a number of; which existed. *2.* These bookshelves, so popular, we've now added, an extra unit.

Ex. 4 Examples: *1.* Subject: computers. Are computers fairly commonplace today? Yes, they are. No, they aren't. *2.* Subject: We. Have we (*or* Do we have) a computer here? Yes, we have. No, we haven't (*or* we don't). *4.* Do these programs have to be changed . . .? (*or, sometimes,* Have these programs to be changed . . .?)

S V O
Ex. 5 Examples: *1.* Full-scale computers/have/a large number of pro-
S V O A
grams. *2.* We/must change/all the programs/tomorrow.

S V S V C
Ex. 6 Examples: *1.* I/don't believe/that [those bookshelves/ are/popular/
A A O S V V C O
anywhere /yet] (O). *2.* [What that advertisement/says] (S) is not/true. *3.* [What
S V S A V
that advertisement/says] (O) I/simply/don't believe.

Ex. 7 *1.* Od. *2.* Cs. *3.* a. Od; b. Co. *4.* a. Od; b. Co. *5.* a. Oi; b. Od. *6.* Co *or* Od. *7.* a. Cs; b. Cs. *8.* a. Od; b. Co. *9.* a. Cs; b. Od; c. Co. *10.* a. Oi; b. Od; c. Od. *11.* Cs. *12.* a. Od; b. Co. *13.* Od. *14.* Cs. *15.* a. Od; b. Co. *16.* Cs. *17.* a. Od; b. Co. *18.* Od. *19.* a. Od; b. Co. *20.* a. Oi; b. Od. *21.* a. Od; b. Co. *22.* a. Oi; b. Od; c. Oi. *23.* a. Od; b. Od. *24.* a. Oi; b. Od.

Ex. 8 *1.* b, c, f. *2.* a, c, e. *3.* a, c, e. *4.* b, d, e. *5.* 1. b, c, f. 2. b, c, f. *6.* b, d, e. *7.* b, d, g. *8.* a, d, e. *9.* b, d, f. *10.* b, d, g. *11.* b, d, h. *12.* b, d, h.

Ex. 9 *1.* intensive. *2.* a. intensive; b. extensive. *3.* extensive. *4.* a. dynamic; b. stative. *5.* a. monotransitive; b. ditransitive; c. complex transitive. *6.* ditransitive. *7.* complex transitive. *8.* intensive. *9.* extensive. *10.* a. dynamic; b. stative.

Ex. 10 Examples: *1.* Samuel Pepys was a writer in the seventeenth century. *2.* Big Ben is by the River Thames in London. *3.* Pepys saw the fire from his home.

Ex. 11 *1.* h. *2.* g. *3.* j. *4.* h. *5.* b. *6.* h. *7.* f. *8.* e. *9.* h. *10.* h. *11.* f. *12.* f. *13.* h. *14.* e. *15.* e. *16.* f. *17.* i. *18.* c. *19.* j. (*or* h.). *20.* a.

Ex. 12

a *noun:* right (2), wrongs (2), cold (1), drink (1), bed, like (1), failing, men, doctor, results (1), growth, weight, development, muscles, fat, hair, towel.
adjective: right (1), cold (2), common, serious, dry (1), warm (2).
adverb: quick, before (3), since, well, thoroughly.
verb: wrongs (1), right (3), cure, go, drink (2), are, taking, results (2),

warm (1), sift, stir, dry (2), comb.
b *article:* the, a.
demonstrative: that (2), this
pronoun: it, you.
preposition: in, with (1), of (1), to, before (2), like (2), as (2), of (2), with (2).
conjunction: that (1), before (1), and, as (1), that (3).

Ex. 13 *1.* stat. *2.* dyn. *3.* dyn. *4.* a. stat.; b. dyn. *5.* a. stat.; b. dyn. *6.* stat. *7.* a. stat.; b. stat. *8.* dyn. *9.* a. dyn.; b. stat. *10.* a. stat.; b. stat.; c. dyn. *11.* a. stat.; b. dyn. *12.* dyn.

Ex. 14 *1.* He. *2.* it. *3.* them. *4.* then. *5.* him. *6.* there. *7.* one. *8.* ones. *9.* some. *10.* did (so). *11.* did. *12.* so. *13.* not. *14.* it. *15.* to. *16.* to. *17.* to (be). *18.* can. *19.* do so. *20.* should.

Ex. 15 *1.* What was sprayed . . . ? *2.* Who wrote . . . ? *3.* What did he write? *4.* What did he write an account of? *5.* Where did the fire start? *6.* How did it burn? *7.* How long did it burn? *8.* When did that happen? *9.* Whose account of it . . . ? *10.* How often did fires break out . . . ? *11.* How many people . . . ? *12.* How much rain . . . ? *13.* How far is it . . . ? *14.* How long will it take me . . . ? *15.* During which century was this castle built? *16.* Why was the Aswan Dam built? *or* For what purpose was . . . ?

Ex. 16 Examples: *1.* non-assertion, interrogative, positive (yet). *2.* non-assertion, negative (yet). *3.* assertion, positive, declarative (already).

Ex. 17 *1.* a. a; b. lexical; c. an; d. auxiliary. *2.* a. item; b. function; c. lexical; d. function; e. primary; f. auxiliary; g. function; h. modal; i. auxiliary. *3.* a. lexical; b. item; c. auxiliary; d. member; e. system. *4.* a. verb; b. syntactic; c. noun; d. inflection. *5.* a. form; b. modal; c. auxiliary; d. function. *6.* a. lexical; b. past; c. tense; d. past; e. participle; f. predict; g. base. *7.* a. defective; b. infinitive; c. *-ing*; d. participle; e. *-ed*; f. participle; g. imperative. *8.* a. past; b. tense; c. past; d. participle; e. predict; f. base. *9.* a. phonological; b. consonant; c. voiced; d. unvoiced. *10.* a. base; b. vowel; c. base; d. vowel; e. inflection; f. voiced; g. unvoiced. *11.* a. tense; b. overt; c. concord; d. number. *12.* a. marked; b. subjunctive; c. mood; d. unmarked; e. indicative; f. mood. *13.* a. lexical; b. indicative; c. mood; d. imperative. *14.* a. first; b. auxiliary; c. an; d. operator. *15.* a. lexical; b. verb; c. modal. *16.* a. perfective; b. aspect; c. passive; d. voice; e. auxiliary; f. verb. *17.* a. auxiliary; b. progressive; c. aspect. *18.* a. infinitive; b. non-finite; c. verb; d. non-finite; e. clause. *19.* a. person; b. tense; c. progressive; d. perfective; e. aspect. *20.* a. formulaic; b. subjunctive; c. mandative; d. subjunctive; e. American; f. English.

Ex. 18 a. See the *Grammar,* section 3.5; etc.

Ex. 19 Examples: a. exceptional; b. exceptional; c. regular in spelling, exceptional in pronunciation; d. regular; etc.

Ex. 20 copies, dan*ces*, echoes, exists, fix*es*, gass*es*; etc.

Ex. 21 Examples: *A. Die*[1], doctor? That *is*[2] the last thing I *intend*[3] to *do*[4].
1. non-finite, infinitive. *2.* finite, present tense, indicative, overt concord,

subject *that*. *3*. finite, present tense, indicative. *4*. non-finite, infinitive. *B*. Die[1], traitor! Every man *found*[2] guilty of treachery *pays*[3] the penalty. *1*. finite, imperative. *2*. non-finite, *-ed* participle. *3*. finite, present tense, indicative, overt concord, subject *every man found guilty of treachery*.

Ex. 22 See *Grammar,* 3.10–3.17.

Ex. 23 See 3.10–3.17.

Ex. 24 Examples: A. *1*. I am never taken to a restaurant (present, pass.). *6*. This exercise must be done again (present, M, pass.). C. *23*. She must have been very unhappy (M, perfective).

Ex. 25 *1*. are we? *2*. aren't I? *3*. don't you? *4*. isn't he? *5*. hasn't he? *6*. hasn't he? *or* doesn't he? *7*. doesn't he? *8*. is there? *9*. has there? *10*. can't you? *11*. didn't you? *12*. didn't we? *13*. won't you? *14*. will there? *15*. wouldn't you? *16*. hadn't you? *17*. wouldn't we? *18*. hadn't you? *19*. did you? *20*. need we?

Ex. 26 *A*. 1. e; 2. a. *B*. 1. b; 2. a. *C*. 1. d; 2. a. *D*. 1. c; 2. f. *E*. 1. c; 2. a. *F*. 1. b; 2. f. *G*. 1. b, c; 2. d. *H*. 1. c; 2. a. *I*. 1. a; 2. c. *J*. 1. e; 2. b, c.

Ex. 27 *A*. 1. f; 2. a. *B*. 1. a; 2. a. *C*. 1. f; 2. b. *D*. 1. f; 2. a. *E*. 1. f; 2. e. *F*. 1. a; 2. c. *G*. 1. a; 2. a. *H*. 1. f; 2. b. *I*. 1. a; 2. a. *J*. 1. a; 2. g. *K*. 1. g; 2. a. *L*. 1. f; 2. a. *M*. 1. a; 2. f. *N*. 1. a; 2. g. *O*. 1. b; 2. b. *P*. 1. f; 2. g. *Q*. 1. d; 2. a. *R*. 1. a; 2. f. *S*. 1. b; 2. a. *T*. 1. g; 2. a.

Ex. 28 *1*. am having; *2*. have; *3*. is just coming; *4*. flows; *5*. is raining; *6*. floats; *7*. is falling; *8*. equals; *9*. is (the train) stopping; *10*. realize, forgive; *11*. is considering; *12*. has; *13*. is dictating; *14*. drives; *15*. am trying; *16*. is dying, is just leaving; *17*. matters; *18*. understand.

Ex. 29 *1*. was drowning, dived, saved; *2*. was listening, rang, did not hear *3*. exploded, was landing, climbed, were waiting, witnessed; *4*. ate, was going; *5*. was still moving (*or* moved), jumped, thought, was happening, ran; *6*. studied; *7*. was always reading, had; *8*. left, were having, did not disturb.

Ex. 30 *1*. have known, have been reading, have not finished; *2*. have been, have you come; *3*. has been learning, has mastered; *4*. has been raining, has stopped; *5*. have remembered.

Ex. 31 *1*. a. No; b. No. *2*. a. Yes; b. No. *3*. a. No; b. No; c. No; d. No; e. Yes; f. No; g. No; h. No; i. No; j. Yes; k. No; l. Yes; m. Yes; n. No; o. Yes; p. No; q. Yes. *4*. a. Yes; b. Yes; c. Yes; d. Yes; e. Yes; f. Yes. *5*. a. No; b. No; c. No.

Ex. 33 *1*. have lived, died, came, was, lived, got. *2*. have been, have not got, were, moved. *3*. received, accepted, have not seen. *4*. Has that man caught, have watched, has not moved. *5*. has been, happened, shot. *6*. has died, never recovered.

Ex. 34 *1*. saw, was, had been ill, had been (*or* was) in bed, (had) had, Had he started. *2*. entered, had fled, had made. *3*. gazed, had come, had seen. *4*. swept, approached, had lain, blazed, were. *5*. went, had taken, was.

Ex. 35 *1*. a. Yes; b. No. *2*. a. No; b. No; c. No. *3*. a. No; b. No; c. No; d. Yes; e. No; f. No. *4*. a. Yes; b. Yes; c. Yes. *5*. a. No; b. No. *6*. a. Yes; b. No. *7*. a. Yes; b. No.

Ex. 36 *1.* (live) a, b, c, d, e, h, i; (be) a, c, h; (have) a, b, c, d, e; (never ring) a, c; (never have) a, b, c. *2.* (have) a, c, d; (be) a, c. *3.* (find) a, b, c; (claim) a, c, d. *4.* (be) a, c, h; (go) g; (hear) a, c. *5.* (leave) a, c; (leave) a, c; (clean) g; (come) a; (do) a, c. *6.* (swim) c, f, h. *7.* (swim) f, g. *8.* (be) a, c, h; (discuss) a, b, c, d, e, f, g, h; (be) a, b, c. *9.* (be) a, c, g; (give) a, c, d, f, g, h; (go) a, c, d, f, g, h; (leave) a, c, d, f, g, h; (catch) a, c, d, f, g, h; (get) a, c, d, f, g, h; (be) a, c; (get back) g. *10.* (show) a, b, c, d, e, f, i. *11.* (get) a, c, d, f, g, h; (stay) a, c, d, f, g, h; (get) c, g; (be) a, c. *12.* (be) a, c, g, h; (be) a, c, h;. *13.* (be opened) a, c, f, g, h; (not be) a, c, h; (keep) g, h.

Ex 37 *1.* a, c. *2.* c, d, e. *3.* e. *4.* (catch) c, d, e; (attend) c, d, e. *5.* c, f. *6.* c, e. *7.* e (were not to). *8.* (be) a, c, e; (discuss) c, d, e.

Ex. 38 *1.* e. *2.* a. *3.* c. *4.* d. *5.* e. *6.* a. *7.* a, a. *8.* b. *9.* e. *10.* d.

Ex. 39 *1.* can type. *2.* can answer. *3.* could never understand. *4.* could solve. *5.* (What you say) might be . . . *6.* Shall I open . . .? *7.* will come. *8.* Would you have . . . ? *9.* will put. *10.* will sit. *11.* would hit. *12.* would sit. *13.* You should read. *14.* We must read. *15.* You must not smoke. *16.* Can you do. *17.* Should we wait. *18.* We need not attend. *19.* That will be. *20.* that must be.

Ex. 40 *1.* John could. *2.* you could . . . if you wanted. *3.* I might be. *4.* if you would . . . we should. *5.* would keep. *6.* you should. *7.* everyone must (*or* had to). *8.* needn't *or* didn't need to. *9.* would be . . . we were looking. *10.* must be *or* must have been.

Ex. 41 *1.* You could. *2.* You could have stayed. *3.* had to. *4.* dare(d). *5.* could have let, you wanted. *6.* should have read. *7.* could have gone. *8.* must have been. *9.* might have been. *10.* would.

Ex. 42 *1.* Could, May, Might. *2.* might, could. *3.* None. *4.* could. *5.* will. *6.* must. *7.* None. *8.* Would. *9.* *None.* *10.* ought to. *11.* *None.* *12.* would. *13.* Zero. *14.* will(?) *15.* *should* replaceable by *ought to; would* not replaceable here. *16.* should. *17.* might, can, could. *18.* *None.*

Ex. 43 *1.* He is able to *or* has permission to. *2.* is able to *or* may. *3.* were able to *or* perhaps we can. *4.* perhaps you will *or* have permission to. *5.* would be *or* ought to be. *6.* ought to be *or* probably are. *7.* will be going to *or* you must. *8.* are obliged to be *or* undoubtedly are. *9.* will actually be there by that time *or* have perhaps arrived. *10.* Will we be seeing him *or* I suggest we see him.

Ex. 44 *1.* he may be coming. *2.* he may have arrived. *3.* I couldn't have remembered it. *4.* I may have been mistaken. *5.* he might have been asleep. *6.* he must have been dozing. *7.* you ought to have been attending. *8.* you ought to have finished. *9.* he ought not to have been smoking. *10.* he should have seen it. *11.* he will be there. *12.* he will have got there. *13.* they would be *or* have been having. *14.* they couldn't have heard you. *15.* I might have been mistaken. *16.* I can't have been mistaken.

Ex. 45 See 4.5.

Ex. 46 *1.* all, half. *2.* all, both, half. *3.* All, Both, Half. *4.* Both. *5.* All, Both, Half. *6.* all, both. *7.* All, Both, Half. *8.* All, Half. *9.* all. *10.* all, both. *11.* all, both. *12*. all, both, half. *13*. all, half. *14*. all. *15*. all, both.

Ex. 47 See 4.13.

Ex. 48 *1*. a. gen; b. gen. *2*. spec. *3*. spec. *4*. gen. *5*. gen. *6*. spec. *7*. gen. *8*. spec. *9*. gen. *10*. spec.

Ex. 49 See 4.18.

Ex. 50 *1*. a. 0; b. 0; c. 0. *2*. a. a; b. a; c. a; d. 0. *3*. a. 0; b. 0 *or* the; c. 0; d. a; e. the; f. 0; g. 0. *4*. a. 0; b. 0; c. 0 *or* the; d. 0 *or* the; e. the; f. 0. *5*. a. 0; b. 0 *or* the; c. the; d. 0. *6*. a. 0 *or* the; b. the; c. the. *7*. a. the; b. the; c. 0; d. 0; e. 0; f. a; g. the. *8*. a. 0; b. an; c. 0; d. 0; e. 0; f. 0; g. 0; h. 0 *or* a; i. an; j. a; k. a; l. the. *9*. a. 0; b. 0; c. 0; d. the; e. the; f. 0 *or* the. *10*. a. 0; b. the; c. the; d. the; *11*. a. 0; b. the; c. 0. *12*. a. the; b. the; c. the; d. the; e. the; f. the; g. 0. *13*. a. 0; b. 0; c. 0; d. 0; e. 0. *14*. a. the; b. a; c. 0; d. 0 *or* a; e. a; f. 0. *15*. a. a; b. 0; *16*. a. 0; b. 0; c. 0; d. a; e. 0; f. a; g. the; h. the. *17*. a. the; b. the; c. the; d. the. *18*. a. the; b. the; c. 0; d. the. *19*. a. 0; b. 0; c. the; d. 0; e. the; f. the; g. 0; h. the. *20*. a. the; b. 0; c. the; d. a; e. a. *21*. a. the; b. 0; c. 0; d. 0; e. the; f. 0; g. 0; h. the; i. the. *22*. a. 0; b. 0; c. the *or* a; d. a; e. the; f. the. *23*. a. 0; b. the; c. the; d. the; e. the. *24*. a. a; b. a; c. 0. *25*. a. 0; b. 0; c. 0 *or* the; d. 0; e. 0; f. 0; g. the; h. the. *26*. a. 0; b. 0 *or* the; c. the; d. the. *27*. a. a; b. 0; c. a; d. 0; e. a; f. the; g. 0; h. the. *28*. a. 0; b. the; c. the; d. the; e. 0; f. 0; g. the *or* 0. *29*. a. a; b. the *or* 0; c. a; d. a; e. the; f. a; g. the. *30*. a. The *or* 0; b. 0; c. the; d. 0.

Ex. 51 *1*. rivalry. *2*. The driver must produce his certificate to the customs. *3*. The soldier left his arms in the barracks. *4*. *No change*. *5*. A goods train carries a heavier load than a truck does.

Ex. 52 *1*. are. *2*. support *or* supports. *3*. is, isn't it? *4*. have. *5*. don't. *6*. were. *7*. are. *8*. was. *9*. has. *10*. is. *11*. has. *12*. are. *13*. are. *14*. do. *15*. cause.

Ex. 53 *1*. Crises often occur in the best regulated families. *2*. Other criteria are needed in analysing these phenomena. *3*. The anonymous workmen were the real heroes on the campuses. *4*. The runners-up were given pound notes. *5*. The skeletons found in the lower strata were taken at once to the museums.

Ex. 54 See 4.31–4.57.

Ex. 55 *1*. X = who *or* that; Y = he. *2*. X = who *or* that; Y = he *or* she. *3*. X = who *or* that; Y = she. *4*. X = who; Y = he *or* she. *5*. X = which; Z = its. *6*. X = who; Z = their. *7*. X = which *or* that; Y = it. *8*. X = who; Y = they. *9*. X = which; Z = its; Y = it. *10*. Z = her *or* its; Y = she *or* it. *11*. X = who; Z = their. *12*. X = which; Z = its *or* her.

Ex. 56 *1*. The story that J. tells, or (has) told, or will tell. *2*. The present that J. gave, has given or will give, or(has) received. *3*. The mistake that J. makes or (has) made. *4*. The punishment that J. (has) received or will receive, or that John administers etc. *5*. The supper that J. has or (has) had. *6*. The consent that he has given, gave or will give. *7*. The interest that he takes etc. *8*. The conclusion that he comes to etc. *9*. The influence that he has or exerts, etc. *10*. The murder that he suffered or committed.

Ex. 57 *2*. Thomas's sister. *3*. Sophocles' plays *or* The plays of S. *4*. Keats' poetry. *5*. The cow's milk. *6*. The captain's error. *7*. The ship's siren. *8*. The noise of the siren. *9*. Somebody's hat. *10*. The name of something. *11*. The history of the school *or* The school's history. *12*. The problems of the world *or* The world's problems. *13*. The art treasures of Europe *or* Europe's art treasures. *14*. A week's holiday. *15*. A year's work. *16*. My brother-in-law's house. *17*. My parents' consent. *18*. The name of the man over there. *19*. The pages of this book. *20*. This evening's newspaper.

Ex. 58 *1*. John is a friend of mine. *2*. —— *3*. That dog of Jack's has . . . *4*. Where is that key of yours? *5*. —— *6*. Those new shoes of yours look . . . *7*. —— *8*. This book of John Christie's is . . . *9*. —— *10*. These exercises of yours are . . .

Ex. 59 *1*. a. It; b. my; c. I; d. it; e. I; f. it; g. my; h. it; i. mine. *2*. a. one's (*or* his); b. it; c. oneself (*or* himself); d. you; e. it; f. it; g. itself. *3*. a. I; b. me; c. herself. *4*. a. their; b. ours; c. our; d. theirs. *5*. a. her; b. his; c. his; d. she; e. hers; f. herself; g. he. *6*. a. its; b. itself; c. them; d. them; e. our. *7*. a. you; b. it; c. me; d. its.

Ex. 60 *1*. themselves. *2*. herself. *3*. her. *4*. yourself. *5*. yourselves. *6*. us. *7*. ourselves. *8*. oneself (*or* himself). *9*. oneself (*or* himself). *10*. myself. *11*. themselves. *12*. himself. *13*. them. *14*. us. *15*. him. *16*. himself.

Ex. 61 *1*. that, which, 0. *2*. which. *3*. that, which, 0. *4*. which. *5*. that, who. *6*. that, who(m), 0. *7*. whom. *8*. whose. *9*. What. *10*. who, that.

Ex. 62 *1*. what. *2*. which. *3*. Who. *4*. Which. *5*. Which. *6*. What, Which. *7*. whose, what. *8*. What. *9*. Whom. *10*. To whom and to which department . . .

Ex. 63 *1*. Every, Each. *2*. every, each. *3*. each. *4*. Each. *5*. Every, Each. *6*. Each. *7*. every. *8*. each. *9*. each. *10*. each.

Ex. 64 *1*. a. some; b. something. *2*. a. any; b. nothing. *3*. a. it all; b. anything. *4*. a. anywhere; b. everywhere. *5*. a. somewhere; b. nowhere. *6*. a. anything; b. Some; c. nothing; d. something. *7*. a. any *or* some; b. some; c. none *or* all. *8*. a. Some; b. everyone; c. everyone *or* anyone; d. some; e. everyone. *9*. a. either; b. neither; c. no. *10*. a. Every; b. They all; c. them all.

Ex. 65 *1*. isn't anything. *2*. scarcely any. *3*. if . . . any. *4*. not . . . any. *5*. seldom . . . any. *6*. Is there anyone? *7*. Before . . . any. *8*. Is there anywhere? *9*. Unless . . . anything. *10*. prevent . . . any.

Ex. 67 *1*. adv. *2*. adj. *3*. adv. *4*. adj. *5*. adj. *6*. adj. *7*. adj. *8*. adv. *9*. adj. *10*. adj. *or* adv. *11*. adj. *12*. adv. *13*. adj. *14*. adj. *15*. adv. *16*. adv. *17*. adj. *18*. adv. *19*, adj. *20*. adj.

Ex. 68 *1*. married students. *2*. students interested. *3*. people involved. *4*. women present. *5*. nearest doctor. *6*. doctor concerned. *7*. seats available *or* available seats. *8*. something really interesting. *9*. much more complicated problem. *10*. much more complicated problem than that *or* problem much more complicated than that. *11*. best road to take. *12*. most difficult people to understand *or* people most difficult to understand. *13*. a person so difficult

to understand *or* so difficult a person to understand. *14*. anyone more difficult. *15*. somewhere really quiet.
Ex. 69 *1*. a. the rich; b. the poor. *2*. The injured. *3*. —— *4*. a. the blind; b. the blind. *5*. —— *6*. —— *7*. the dead. *8*. the living. *9*. the unknown. *10*. the unexpected. *11*. the disabled. *12*. a. the unspeakable; b. the uneatable *or* the inedible. *13*. a. The wise; b. —— *14*. the sick. *15*. the latest.
Ex. 70 *1*. Eager to begin the climb, the men rose . . . *2*. The summit, bare and bleak, towered . . . *3*. —— *4*. . . . a ledge narrow enough for one man. *5*. Thoroughly exhausted, they crawled . . . *6*. Stiff in every joint, they . . . *7*. When fresh, the snow afforded . . . *8*. The wind, keen as a razor, drove . . . *9*. Though light as a feather, their tent somehow remained firm. *10*. . . . brought them down to the base camp, half-dead with the cold.
Ex. 71 *1*. a. Yes; b. Yes. *2*. a. No; b. Yes. *3*. a. No; b. Yes. *4*. a. Yes; b. No. *5*. a. No; b. No. *6*. a. No; b. Yes. *7*. a. No; b. Yes. *8*. a. No; b. Yes. *9*. a. Yes; b. No. *10*. a. No; b. Yes. *11*. a. Yes; b. No. *12*. a. No; b. No.
Ex. 72 *1*. A. *2*. B. *3*. E. *4*. A. *5*. A. *6*. E. *7*. F. *8*. B. *9*. F. *10*. D. *11*. C. *12*. F. *13*. F. *14*. E. *15*. F. *16*. B. *17*. E. *18*. C. *19*. F. *20*. D.
Ex. 73 *1*. a, b. *2*. —— *3*. b. *4*. a, b, c. *5*. a, b, d. *6*. a, b, d. *7*. b. *8*. a, b, c. *9*. —— *10*. b. *11*. —— *12*. a, b, c, d. *13*. b. *14*. —— *15*. b. *16*. a, b, c. *17*. a, b, c. *18*. a, b. *19*. a, b. *20*. b, c.
Ex. 74 Note: crueller, cruellest; drier, driest; more real, most real.
Ex. 75 *1*. a, b, c. *2*. a, b. *3*. a, b, c. *4*. a, b. *5*. a, b, c. *6*. a, b. *7*. a, b. *8*. a, b. *9*. a, b. *10*. a, b, c. *11*. a, b. *12*. a, b, c. *13*. b, c. *14*. b, c. *15*, a, b, c. *16*. a, b, c. *17*. a, b, c. *18*. a, b. *19*. a, b, c. *20*. a, b.
Ex. 76 *1*. well- *or* soundly-. *2*. well- *or* badly-. *3*. well- *or* badly-. *4*. well- *or* badly-. *5*. well-, clearly- *or* ill-. *6*. well- *or* ill-. *7*. well- *or* badly-. *8*. well- *or* badly-. *9*. un(expected). *10*. good- *or* ill-. *11*. well- *or* ill-. *12*. well-, badly- *or* ill-. *13*. well-. *14*. well-, badly- *or* ill-. *15*. well- *or* badly-. *16*. well- *or* badly-. *17*. clean-. *18*. well- *or* badly-. *19*. well-, badly- *or* ill-. *20*. well-, badly- *or* poorly-.
Ex. 77 *1*. J. drives carefully. *2*. S. pronounces E. vowels very well. *3*. D. behaves more courteously than B. *4*. . . . B. speaks (the) more clearly. *5*. B. works very much harder. *6*. B. does not run nearly so (*or* as) fast. *7*. R. approaches his subject far less scientifically. *8*. H. dances most brilliantly. *9*. . . . impressed me considerably. *10*. . . . the person who bids highest . . . *11*. . . . J. teaches in a much more friendly way *or* manner than . . . *12*. The number of street accidents has increased much more rapidly in . . .
Ex. 78 *1*. quickly, A. *2*. quite, B. *3*. a. surprisingly, C; b. well, A. *4*. hardly, F. *5*. rather, F. *6*. once, G. *7*. right, D. *8*. afterwards, G. *9*. honestly, A. *10*. honestly, H. *11*. yet, A. *12*. yet, I. *13*. a. soon, A; b. though, I. *14*. a. so, C; b. early, A. *15*. almost, D. *16*. almost, F. *17*. about, E. *18*. naturally, H. *19*. a. really, H, C or B; b. very, B. *20*. a. In fact, H; b. quite, F.
Ex. 79 *1*. . . . afraid of falling . . . *2*. . . . amused at you(r) meeting . . . *3*. . . . not aware of giving you . . . *4*. . . . confident of winning . . . *5*. . . . decided on

dropping the matter . . . *6*. . . . determined on having . . . *7*. . . . grateful to you for taking . . . *8*. . . . sorry about L's resignation. *9*. . . . sure about S's disappearance? *10*. . . . surprised at him/his getting married . . . *11*. . . . assure you of my willingness . . . *12*. . . . convinced everyone of his innocence. *13*. . . . inform you of the change of plans? *14*. . . . remind you of your responsibility . . . *15*. . . . told me of these problems.

Ex. 80 *1*. Our plans depend on what the Government decides . . . *2*. Our protest is due to the fact that . . . *3*. I was not aware of the fact that . . . *4*. I am fully conscious of the fact that . . . *5*. I am interested in why you want . . . *6*. I am interested (in the fact) that . . . *7*. . . . are very sensitive to who is . . . *8*. I am not sure about what started . . . *9*. I have no doubt about where he . . . *10*. I apologize for the fact that . . . *11*. The disease was clearly related to the fact that . . . *12*. Don't worry about where you can . . .

Ex. 81 Examples: *1*. What our plans depend on is what the G. decides. *2*. What our protest is due to is (the fact) that we . . . *3*. What I was not aware of is (the fact) that his . . . *5*. What I am interested in is why . . . *6*. What I am interested in is (the fact) that you . . . *12*. What you needn't worry about is where . . .

Ex. 82 Examples: *1*. a. Who (*or* Which man) did you give my letter to? b. The man I gave your letter to was that very handsome-looking one.

Ex. 83 Examples: *1*. Have all the breakages been accounted for? *7*. I don't like being stared at like that. *8*. . . . you are likely to be shot at. *10*. But he was not voted for, *or* . . . the candidate who was voted for.

Ex. 84 *1*. past. *2*. —— *3*. in. *4*. —— *5*. —— *6*. off. *7*. inside. *8*. on. *9*. —— *10*. across. *11*. over. *12*. —— *13*. outside. *14*. by. *15*. through. *16*. —— *17*. in front. *18*. opposite. *19*. out. *20*. ——

Ex. 85 *1*. at the bank, a (*or* c). *2*. with him, a; at a restaurant, a. *3*. in the afternoon, a; to Boston, a. *4*. at home, a (*or* c). *5*. at a medical school, a. *6*. at the hospital, b; of practical jokes, d. *7*. in pain, b; from their doctor, a. *8*. at my first operation, a. *9*. as a result, a. *10*. in fact, a. *11*. In all fairness, a; from violent pains, c; in the head, b. *12*. In any case, a; in 1927, a; over the retirement age, a (*or* c).

Ex. 86 *1*. a. to *or* in(to); b. at. *2*. a. at; b. to. *3*. a. to; b. at. *4*. a. on; b. off. *5*. a. on; b. off. *6*. a. (away) from; b. away from. *7*. a. from; b. to. *8*. a. at (*or* in); b. out of. *9*. a. in; b. to *or* into. *10*. a. in; b. to *or* into. *11* a. in; b. at; c. from; d. to. *12*. a. at; b. to.

Ex. 87 *1*. below. *2*. in front of. *3*. over. *4*. above. *5*. a. over; b. under. *6*. after. *7*. behind. *8*. a. on top of; b. under(neath) *or* beneath. *9*. a. above; b. below *or* beneath. *10*. a. on top of; b. above *or* behind; c. over.

Ex. 88 *1*. a. across; b. through. *2*. a. across; b. along. *3*. a. across *or* along; b. through. *4*. a. along; b. through; c. across; d. past. *5*. a. across; b. through.

Ex. 89 *1*. c. *2*. b. *3*. b *or* a. *4*. a. *5*. g. *6*. c. *7*. e. *8*. d. *9*. b. *10*. a. *11*. c. *12*. b. *13*. f. *14*. c. *15*. a. *16*. d. *17*. a. *18*. c. *19*. b. *20*. e.

Ex. 90 *1.* a. into; b. in. *2.* a. in; b. out of. *3.* a. in; b. out of. *4.* a. beneath; b. beneath. *5.* a. over; b. under. *6.* a. under; b. in (*or* under). *7.* a. in; b. beyond. *8.* a. past; b. from. *9.* a. above; b. below. *10.* a. from; b. to. *11.* a. beyond *or* out of; b. into; c. past *or* beyond; d. in.
Ex. 91 *1.* a. on; b. at; c. until; d. by. *2.* a. In; b. in; c. for; d. from; e. until. *3.* a. For; b. since. *4.* a. on; b. on. *5.* a. until; b. before; c. At; d. by; e. after. *6.* a. For; b. before *or* after.
Ex. 92 *1.* a. 0; b. (on). *2.* a. 0; b. on. *3.* a. 0; b. (on). *4.* a. 0; b. 0. *5.* a. (on); b. (on).
Ex. 93 *1.* (for). *2.* (for). *3.* (for). *4.* for. *5.* For. *6.* (for). *7.* for. *8.* for. *9.* (for). *10.* a. For; b. for.
Ex. 94 Examples: *1.* . . . because of the intense heat. *2.* . . . for fear of . . . *3.* On account of his knowledge of . . . *4.* . . . out of sympathy for . . . *5.* . . . either from starvation or from severe wounds. *6.* . . . for money.
Ex. 95 *1.* like. *2.* as. *3.* like. *4.* as. *5.* like. *6.* as. *7.* like. *8.* Like *or* As. *9.* with. *10.* without. *11.* without. *12.* with. *13.* with. *14.* by. *15.* with. *16.* without. *17.* by. *18.* a. with; b. by. *19.* by. *20.* at. *21.* with. *22.* by. *23.* at. *24.* with. *25.* at. *26.* at. *27.* a. against; b. for (*or* a. for; b. against). *28.* with *or* for. *29.* with. *30.* against. *31.* a. for; b. against. *32.* a. with; b. in. *33.* a. with; b. with; c. in. *34.* a. with; b. without. *35.* a. of; b. with. *36.* a. of *or* with; b. without.
Ex. 96 *1.* Despite the city's many attractions, . . . *2.* In spite of the clear scientific evidence, people . . . *3.* Notwithstanding the provision (made) in Article 6 for compensating a tenant etc., the landlord will not be . . . *4.* . . . for all his immense fortune. *5.* With all your huge secretarial staff, it still seems . . .
Ex. 97 *1.* c, f, g. *2.* b, c. *3.* a, b, d, e, f, g. *4.* c. *5.* c. *6.* b. *7.* b, d, e, g.
Ex. 98 *1.* d. *2.* f. *3.* e. *4.* c. *5.* a. *6.* e. *7.* b. *8.* g. *9.* g. *10.* f. *11.* d. *12.* a. *13.* b. *14.* c. *15.* g. *16.* e. *17.* a. *18.* d. *19.* f. *20.* a. *21.* a. *22.* b. *23.* d. *24.* f. *25.* e. *26.* g.
Ex. 99 *1.* obl. *2.* opt. *3.* obl. *4.* opt. *5.* obl. *6.* obl. *7.* opt. *8.* obl. *9.* obl. *10.* obl. *11.* opt. *12.* obl. *13.* obl. *14.* opt. *15.* opt. *16.* obl. *17.* obl. *18.* obl. *19.* opt. *20.* obl.
Ex. 100 *1.* d. *2.* g. *3.* e. *4.* e. *5.* f. *6.* d. *7.* e. *8.* g. *9.* c. *10.* g.
Ex. 101 *1.* of you. *2.* to *or* for you. *3.* with you. *4.* for you. *5.* for me. *6.* to all our friends. *7.* for you. *8.* to *or* for me. *9.* to me. *10.* to *or* for me.
Ex. 102 *1.* g. *2.* a. *3.* b. *4.* h. *5.* c. *6.* d. *7.* d. *8.* e. *9.* a. *10.* g. *11.* h. *12.* g. *13.* h. *14.* d. *15.* c. *16.* b. *17.* e. *18.* d. *19.* b. *20.* f.
Ex. 103 *1.* The dam blew up. *2.* My glasses have broken. *3.* My roses have died. *4.* That picture has moved. *5.* The bell rang. *6.* The car rolled down . . . *7.* My broken arm set easily. *8.* The gate shut quickly. *9.* The train stopped. *10.* This screw won't turn.
Ex. 104 *1.* a. *2.* b. *3.* c. *4.* b. *5.* a. *6.* c. *7.* b. *8.* b. *9.* a. *10.* b.
Ex. 105 *1.* has. *2.* depend(s). *3.* are. *4.* is. *5.* is. *6.* are. *7.* is. *8.* are. *9.* is *or* are. *10.* is *or* are. *11.* were. *12.* is. *13.* are *or* is. *14.* deserve(s) *15.* has. *16.* has *or* have. *17.* is. *18.* is. *19.* knows. *20.* are.

Ex. 106 *1.* its *or* their. *2.* its. *3.* his (*or* ?their). *4.* their. *5.* a good friend *or* good friends. *6.* a. she; b. his. *7.* a. he *or* she; b. his *or* her. *8.* either alternative. *9.* it . . . too high *or* they . . . unnecessary.

Ex. 107 *1.* haven't . . . yet. *2.* isn't anyone. *3.* hasn't anything. *4.* did not produce . . . on any of them. *5.* does not apply . . . to any . . . yet. *6.* has not revealed . . . anything . . . *7.* . . . does not help us . . . at all . . . either. *8.* We need not go far to find anyone . . . *or* don't have to go far . . . *9.* R. is not yet living . . . *10.* He has not been away very long. *11.* . . . cannot find anywhere . . . *12.* . . . hasn't ever given me any . . . *13.* There are not many people . . . yet. *14.* I cannot understand either . . . *15.* I cannot understand any . . .

Ex. 108 *1.* I don't think it has anything . . . *2.* We need seldom go far to find anyone . . . *or* We seldom need to go far . . . *3.* It has scarcely revealed anything . . . *4.* Only two of us have had any . . . *5.* I am against making any concession(s) . . . *6.* I rarely see anything good . . . *7.* Few people have ever given an honest answer . . . *8.* I forgot to bring any . . . *9.* There is very little hope of finding any . . . *10.* I am unaware of any opposition . . .

Ex. 109 *1.* Never have we heard . . . *2.* Seldom do we receive . . . *3.* Scarcely ever, in the past, did this nation face . . . *4.* Never before were we asked . . . *5.* Rarely is there an . . . *6.* Only then shall we begin . . .

Ex. 110 Examples: *1.* a. Many people did not attend, ie many stayed away; b. Not many people attended, ie few did. *2.* a. All the people were not at work, ie either everyone was absent, or not everyone was there; b. Not all the people were at work, ie not everyone was there. *5.* a. One . . . didn't hear . . .; b. Not one heard, ie none heard.

Ex. 111 Examples: *1.* a. I lend to none; b. I only lend to a select few. *2.* a. Nothing that glitters is gold; b. Only some of the things that glitter are gold. *3.* a. Half is uncompleted still; b. We haven't completed even half yet.

Ex. 112 *1.* can't/type. *2.* can't/use. *3.* can't/be. *4.* may/not be. *5.* can't/have arrived. *6.* ought/not to behave. *7.* needn't/be alarmed. *8.* will/not be. *9.* will/not listen. *10.* must/not leave.

Paraphrases: *1.* S. is not able to type . . . *2.* She won't be allowed to . . . *3.* I am sure they're not far away . . . *4.* It is possible that I shan't be . . . *5.* It isn't possible that they have . . . *6.* It's your duty not to behave like that. *7.* There's no need for you to be . . . *8.* They aren't going to be . . . *9.* He refuses to listen . . . *10.* You're obliged not to leave . . .

Ex. 113 *1.* pos. *2.* neg. *3.* pos. *4.* neg. *5.* pos. *6.* pos. *7.* neg. *8.* pos. *9.* neg. Examples of paraphrase: *1.* I am expecting some letters: have they arrived? *2.* I don't think there is any reason for staying here.

Ex. 114 See 7.48 *and* 7.50.

Ex. 115 *1.* b. *2.* a. *3.* b. *4.* b. *5.* a. *6.* b. *7.* a. *8.* a *or* b. *9.* b. *10.* a.

Ex. 116 Examples: *1.* Where must one go to see . . . ? *2.* How much did Europeans know . . . before 1911? *3.* In what year was it rediscovered? *4.* Who discovered it? *5.* What was the discoverer's surname? *6.* What nationality was he? *7.* For how long had the city been buried? *8.* How deep was the canyon?

Ex. 117 See 7.44–7.57.

Ex. 118 *1.* —— *2.* You. *3.* All the men over twenty-one. *4.* Somebody. *5.* —— *6.* —— *7.* you. *8.* —— *9.* each man. *10.* anyone.

Ex. 119 Examples: *1.* I feel the weather we're having is very beautiful. Don't you? *2.* I have waited so long (so anxiously, so eagerly) for this moment. *3.* I suggest you have some dinner with me. Would you like to? *4.* The last thing I want to do is to tempt you . . . *5.* Once you start paying out money, you find yourself paying a lot. *6.* If you don't waste things, you won't be poor. *7.* Now we come to the . . . *8.* If something is to be done, I think it should be done as soon as possible. *9.* Here is information about what you should see in Paris. *10.* Warning: you will soon come to a part of the road where men are working.

Ex. 120 *1.* S+V. *2.* S+V+Od+A. *3.* S+V+Od+A. *4.* S+V+Od *5.* S+(V). *6.* S+(V). *7.* S+A. *8.* S+V. *9.* S+V+Od+Co. *10.* S+Cs+A. *1.* A war has started over the prices of holidays. *5.* The immigration rules have been criticized. *6.* Oil pollution measures are to be tested.

Ex. 121 Examples: *1.* F. arrived unexpectedly. *2.* He arrived one morning. *3.* . . . in April. *4.* F. felt relieved, though he was . . . *5.* He had come to take . . . *6.* Herr S. welcomed him, wishing to appear friendly. *7.* S., though surprised by F's arrival, welcomed him warmly. *8.* F., unaware of his host's annoyance, felt relieved.

Ex. 122 *1.* a, b. *2.* a. *3.* a, b. *4.* a. *5.* —— *6.* a. *7.* a, b. *8.* a. *9.* —— *10.* a.

Ex. 123 Examples: *1.* a. early; b. late. *2.* a. in the morning; b. in the evening. *3.* a. coolly; b. warmly. *4.* a. fluently; b. haltingly. *5.* a. quickly; b. gradually. *6.* a. hard; b. without strain. *7.* a. at once; b. eventually. *8.* a. publicly; b. in the drawing-room. *9.* a. frankly; b. evasively. *10.* a. well; b. with difficulty.

Ex. 124 *1.* . . . and so does his son. *2.* . . . and so did Ilsa. *3.* . . . and so can you. *4.* eg gradually. *5.* eg in the morning. *6.* eg haltingly. *7.* eg greatly. *8.* eg in the evening. *9.* eg charmingly. *10.* It was in April that he arrived. *11.* It was with difficulty that . . . *12.* It was only in the drawing-room that . . .

Ex. 125 See 8.5.

Ex. 126 Examples: *1.* in the framework of society; place adjunct, position. *2.* now; time adjunct, time when. *3.* haltingly, manner adjunct process. *For the remainder,* see 8.6–8.44.

Ex. 127 Examples: *1.* extremely. *2.* exceedingly. *3.* far. *4.* greatly. *5.* actually. *6.* badly. *7.* absolutely. *8.* bitterly. *9.* deeply. *10.* definitely. *11.* completely. *12.* entirely. *13.* heartily. *14.* fully. *15.* keenly. *16.* highly. *17.* violently. *18.* well. *19.* utterly. *20.* totally.

Ex. 128 *1.* I. *2.* M1. *3.* M2, F. *4.* M1. *5.* M2. *6.* M1/M2. *7.* F.

Ex. 129 *1.* F, M2, I. *2.* I, F. *3.* M1. *4.* F. *5.* premodifying *angry*. *6.* F, M2. *7.* M1/M2. *8.* F, M1/M2. *9.* I, F, M1/M2. *10.* F. *11.* F. *12.* M2, I, F. *13.* F. *14.* premodifying *impossible*. *15.* M2, M1. *16.* M2. *18.* M2, F. *19.* F. *20.*

M2. *21*. F. *22*. M1/M2, F, I. *23*. F. *24*. M1/M2, F. *25*. F. *26*. F: painted badly *or* badly painted. *27*. F. *28*. F, I. *29*. M1/M2, F, I. *30*. M2.

Ex. 130 *1*. a. ONly fiNANcial matters; b. ONly at our SUB-committee meeting; c. ONly on THURSdays *or* on THURSdays ONly. *2*. It is only financial matters that . . . It is only at our sub-committee meeting . . . It is only on Thursdays . . .

Ex. 131 *1*. a. ONly a man's REAL influence . . . It is only a man's real influence . . .; b. . . . is ONly exerted AFTer his DEATH. It is only after his death that . . . *2*. a. We can ONly expect to save our OWN HOMES . . .; b. . . . ONly by SUCH a STRATegy. *3*. a. The G. has ALso made THIS anNOUNCement . . .; b. . . . through the PRESS ALso.

Ex. 132 *1*. dir. *2*. pos. *3*. dir. *4*. pos. *5*. dir. *6*. dir. *7*. pos. *8*. pos. *9*. dir. *10*. pos. *11*. dir. *12*. dir.

Ex. 133 *1*. a. *2*. b. *3*. a, b. *4*. a. *5*. a. *6*. b. *7*. a. *8*. b. *9*. a. *10*. b.

Ex. 134 *1*. A, b; B, a. *2*. A, b; B, a. *3*. A, a; B, b. *4*. A, a; B, b. *5*. A, b; B, ——. *6*. A, a; B, ——. *7*. A, b; B, a. *8*. A, a *or* b; B, b. *9*. A, a; B, b. *10*. A, a; B, b.

Ex. 135 *1*, a. *2*, a. *3*, b. *4*, b. *5*, a. *6*, b. *7*, b. *8*, b. *9*, a. *10*, b.

Ex. 136 *1*. A, b; B, a. *2*. A, b; B, a. *3*. A, b; B, a. *4*. A, a; B, b. *5*. A, a; B, b. *6*. A, b; B, a. *7*. A, a; B, ——. *8*. A, a; B, b.

Ex. 137 *1*. since. *2*. since. *3*. for. *4*. till. *5*. for. *6*. since. *7*. for, since. *8*. since. *9*. For. *10*. Till. *11*. For. *12*. for.

Ex. 138 See 8.35.

Ex. 139 *1*. seldom go out. *2*. quite often. *3*. sometimes. *4*. Our students never . . . *5*. very often. *6*. often. *7*. Occasionally they ask . . .

Ex. 140 *1*. a, b. *2*. a, b. *3*. c, f, g.

Ex. 141 *1*. a, f. *2*. a, d, f. *3*. a. *4*. a, d. *5*. a. *6*. a, f. *7*. —— *8*. a, d, f. *9*. f, g. *10*. f, g. *11*. g. *12*. a, g. *13*. f. *14*. f. *15*. f, g. *16*. a, d. g. *17*. a, d. g. *18*. a, f. *19*. f, g. *20*. b, c, g. *21*. a, b, c, d, f, g. *22*. a, f. *23*. a, g. *24*. f. *25*. d, g. *26*. b, c, g. *27*. e, g. *28*. a, d. *29*. f, g. *30*. e, f. g.

Ex. 142 *1*. a. once a month this year; b. This year, . . . *2*. a. twice while you were out; b. While you were out, . . . *3*. a. all the morning every day this week; b. This week, . . . *4*. a. for a day or two several times this summer; b. This summer, . . . *5*. a. for two or three hours at a time almost every day during the winter . . .; b. During the winter . . . *6*. a. between nine and twelve every weekday next month; b. Next month, . . . *7*. a. between two and four during the summer; b. During the summer, . . .

Ex. 143 *1*. normal order: place + time. *2*. normal: more extended period (in 1848) comes last. *3*. normal: process + place. *4*. normal: process + direction. *5*. as for 4. *6*. as for 1. *7*. place adjunct moved to end position for focus. *8*. normal, provided *quietly* refers to *docked*. *9*. long place adjunct comes second, partly for balance, mainly to avoid ambiguity. *10*. process comes after place for balance and focus.

Ex. 144 *1*. a. *2*. b. *3*. b. *4*. a. *5*. a. *6*. a. *7*. b. *8*. b. *9*. a. *10*. b.

Ex. 145 *1*. a. *2*. c. *3*. c. *4*. b. *5*. b. *6*. c. *7*. a. *8*. b. *9*. a. *10*. a.

Ex. 146 Examples: *1*. Nevertheless. *2*. However. *3*. On the contrary. *4*. First *5*. similarly. *6*. on the one hand, on the other hand. *7*. therefore. *8*. hence, for example. *9*. Equally. *10*. at the same time. *11*. for instance. *12*. thereafter.

Ex. 147 See 8.53.

Ex. 148 Omit: *1*. you are. *2*. he was. *3*. that were. *4*. he had been. *5*. he might be. *6*. you were. *7*. the last seven words. *8*. the second *I*; and *take part in it*. *9*. you are. *10*. which was. *11*. rocks which were formed. *12*. it is.

Ex. 149 Add: *1*. I'll. *2*. Did you. *3*. Is. *4*. Did. *5*. Have you. *6*. I'm (sorry), I (had). *7*. Are you. *8*. I. *9*. Is there. *10*. Was there. *11*. Is (there). *12*. I'm.

Ex. 150 *1*. No. *2*. Yes. *3*. No. *4*. Yes. *5*. No. *6*. No. *7*. Yes. *8*. Yes. *9*. No. *10*. Yes.

Ex. 151 Omit: *1*. he. *2*. ____ *3*. the second *because* and the third *he*. *4*. the second *we*. *5*. the second *he*. *6*.____ *7*. the second *he*. *8*.____.

Ex. 152 See 9.16. *1*. (and who) subsequently. *2*. (is) therefore. *3*. (and) indeed. *4*. (and) yet. *5*. (and) then *or* if you do. *6*. (and) moreover. *7*. (that), namely. *8*. (and we) also. *9*. (and) furthermore. *10*. (and) at the same time.

Ex. 153 See 9.17. *1*. (or) if you don't. *2*. else. *3*. at least. *4*. if it is not. *5*. otherwise. *6*. alternatively. *7*. on the other hand. *8*. nevertheless. *9*. in any case. *10*. despite that.

Ex. 154 *1*. Either my old school friends . . . , or they avert . . . *2*. George not only shouted . . . but he also came . . . *3*. The fire destroyed both . . . and . . . *4*. Neither the primitive fire-engines had any effect . . . , nor did pulling down . . . have any result whatever. *5*. Both in 1666 and in 1940 fire-fighters . . . *6*. The city was abandoned neither after the fire of 1666 nor after . . . *7*. I have both given up . . . and given my typewriter away. *8*. I have no objection . . . , but I refuse . . . *9*. . . . you must neither show fear nor dart away . . . *10*. Zoologists thought the strange creature was either a . . . or a . . .

Ex. 155 Omit: *1*. the second occurrence of *the Chinese*. *2*. *they have*. *3*. both occurrences of *it has to be*. *4*. the second *is generally eaten*. *5*. both occurrences of *they are*. *6*. the second *is used for cooking*. *7*. the second *is the best place*. *8*. the second *eat their food*. *9*. the second *(marriages) are often celebrated*. *10*. either the second *include* and the second *on the menu*, or the first *on the menu*, with a comma after *rice*. *11*. the first *from influenza*, and the second *people*. *12*. the last eight words. *13*. either the first *infection* or the second *escape infection*. *14*. the second *of the things around it*. *15*. the first *highly dangerous objects*. *16*. the first *very dangerous*. *17*. the second *is protected from danger*. *18*. the second *hours' sleep a night*. *19*. *of sleep requirements*. *20*. the last three words.

Ex. 156 Omit: *1*. the first phrases. *2*. the first *sentences*. *3*. the second *sentences*. *4*. the first *reasons*. *5*. say *Your experience and mine*. *6*. the second *your*. *7*. the second *his obligations*. *8*. the first *to a pre-arranged plot*.

Ex. 157 *1.* 'red flags, white flags, etc.' or 'tricolour flags'. *2.* they are married to each other or to different spouses. *3.* they both won the same cup, or each won one. *4.* they won nothing jointly or separately. *5.* George and Mary were brother and sister, or not.
Ex. 158 *1.* A. *2.* B, a. *3.* B, a. *4.* B, a. *5.* B, a. *6.* B, a. *7.* B, a. *8.* A. *9.* B, a. *10.* B, a. *11.* B, b. *12.* B, c. *13.* A. *14.* B, a.
Ex. 159 See 10.1–10.36.
Ex. 161 *1.* some. *2.* both. *3.* each (one). *4.* every one. *5.* enough. *6.* yours. *7.* none. *8.* the only one. *9.* the others. *10.* others. *11.* the same (one). *12.* the same (soup). *13.* the one. *14.* the one, the one. *15.* it. *16.* those, mine. *17.* the very one. *18.* that. *19.* those. *20.* all (of them).
Ex. 162 *1.* then. *2.* there. *3.* that. *4.* that. *5.* that way. *6.* (in) that way.
Ex. 163 Examples: *1.* is = pro-form for 3rd pers. sing., present tense, + progressive, of WAIT. *2.* have = pro-form for 1st. pers. sing., present tense of HAVE + Od.
Ex. 164 *1.* I did. But I don't do so now. *2.* I did. But I don't now. *3.* No, I didn't do that. *4.* I did. But I don't now. *5.* I did. But I don't do so now. *6.* No. I didn't do that. *7.* I did. But I don't now. *8.* I did. But I don't do so now.
Ex. 165 *1.* Yes, I remembered to (do so). *2.* Yes, I would prefer to (do so). *3.* Yes, I wish to (do so). *4.* Yes, I would advise you to (do so). *5.* Yes, I expected him to (do so). *6.* Yes, I trust you to (do so). *7.* Yes, I advise it. *8.* Yes, I regret it. *9.* Yes, I caught him (doing so). *10.* Yes, I often see him (doing so).
Ex. 166 Examples: *1.* I think so. I think not. *2.* I believe so. I believe not.
Ex. 167 *1.* pro-form for *that*-clause, in affirmative answer to a question. *2.* B, pro-form for *that*-clause, B agreeing with A's statement; C, pro-form for *that*-clause already mentioned. *3.* pro-form for whole verb phrase in previous clause. *4.* pro-form for two previous sentences. *5.* equivalent of adjective *true* referring to the statement made in previous sentence. *6.* pro-form for complement of BE in previous clause. *7.* pro-form for adjective in the complement of BE in previous clause. *8.* pro-form for *as* + noun complement of BE in previous clause. *9.* do so = pro-form for lexical verb in previous infinitive clause. *10.* conjunct used as conjunction.
Ex. 168 *1.* following, cata. *2.* here, ana. *3.* That, ana. *4.* this, ana. *5.* this, cata. *6.* The above, ana; What follows, cata. *7.* that hypothesis, ana. *8.* such opposition, ana.
Ex. 169 *1.* a. Yes, I have answered that letter; b. Yes, I have answered it; c. Yes, I have done (so); d. Yes, I have; e. Yes. *2.* Yes, he has paid this account, etc. *3.* a. Yes, he has asked for a receipt; b. Yes, he has asked for one, etc. *4.* a. Yes, they will send back the cheque; b. Yes, they will send it back, etc. *1.* a. Of course I have answered . . . *2.* a. He has probably paid . . .; d. He probably has. *3.* a. Perhaps he has asked . . .; d. Perhaps he has. *4.* a. They will send back the cheque eventually; d. They will eventually.

Ex. 170 *1.* a. I answered that letter yesterday; b. I answered it yesterday; c. I did so yesterday; d. I did yesterday; e. Yesterday. *2.* a. He probably paid this account on Friday; b. He probably paid it on Friday; c. He probably did so on Friday; d. He probably did on Friday; e. Probably on Friday. *3.* I usually attend his lectures twice a week; b. I usually attend them twice a week; c. I usually do so twice a week; d. I usually do twice a week; e. Usually twice a week. *4.* Perhaps they will take away this rubbish tomorrow; b. Perhaps they will take it away tomorrow; c. Perhaps they will do so tomorrow; d. Perhaps they will tomorrow; e. Perhaps tomorrow.

Ex. 171 Examples: *1.* Are you sure he has? That's right, he has. *2.* When did you? I'm so glad you have.

Ex. 172 Examples: *1. That you could do it*: finite clause acting as O. *2. That you can do it*: finite clause acting as S. *3. if you try*: finite clause acting as A. *5. Standing here all day*: non-finite, *-ing* participle clause acting as A. *6. Standing here all day*: non-finite, *-ing* participle clause acting as S. *7. to listen to chamber music*: non-finite infinitive clause, acting as C. *10. The long journey over*: non-finite, verbless clause, acting as A. *18. Since I have been . . .*, finite clause, A; *for you now to tell me*: non-finite, infinitive clause, S; *I cannot do so*: finite clause, O. *20. What I wanted to say*: finite clause, S; *as I didn't know*: finite, A; *whether you were going to say*: finite, O; *that you could come or you couldn't*: finite, O.

V A V

Ex. 173 Example: *11.* a. *Glancing up/at my tired face,* or *Glancing up at/my*

O

tired face, acting as A for main clause *(she asked, in a rather grating voice)*;

S V

b. *how I/was feeling,* acting as O of *asked* in the main clause.

Ex. 174 *1.* As it was crossing *or* as I was crossing. *2.* For you to see her *or* For me, or someone else, to see her. *3.* Though we were . . . *or* though they were . . . *4.* We, dressed in white robes . . . *or* the visitors, dressed . . . *5.* I regret that I am speaking now . . . *or* I regret that I spoke . . . *6.* If I walked fast, it could be . . . *or* If you, or someone else, walked . . . *7.* . . . so ill that he was obliged . . . *or* so ill that he is now obliged . . . *8.* . . . for me to finish this *or* . . . for you, or someone else, to . . . *9.* Whether he is here . . . *or* Whether it is here . . . *10.* We were always afraid . . . *or* We are . . .

Ex. 175 See 11.6–11.9. Examples: *1.* that. *2.* that. *3.* if. *5.* non-finite verb *standing*.

Ex. 176 *1.* prep. *2.* sub. *3.* sub. *4.* sub. *5.* prep. *6.* sub. *7.* prep. *8.* sub. *9.* sub. *10.* prep. *11.* prep. *12.* sub.

Ex. 177 *1.* g. *2.* h. *3.* j. *4.* j. *5.* g. *6.* b. *7.* e. *8.* a. *9.* c. *10.* f. *11.* i. *12.* l. *13.* k. *14.* j. *15.* g. *16.* a.

Ex. 178 *1, 4, 5, 7, 9.*

Ex. 179 Examples: *1.* I told you we have only . . .; *that* optional; *that*-clause

O of *told*. *2*. I am very sorry we have . . .; *that* optional; *that*-clause C of *sorry*. *3*. Our conclusion is . . .; *that* optional; *that*-clause C of S. *4*. Our conclusion is that, in view of . . .; *that* obligatory. *5*. Having taken careful measurements, I estimate . . .; *that* optional; *or*, I estimate, having taken . . .; that . . .; *that* obligatory. *6*. That we have only enough . . . is very alarming; *that* oblig.; *that*-clause S of *is*; *or* It is very alarming that we have . . .; *that* oblig.; *that*-clause anticipated by *It*. *7*. Our conclusion, reached after careful checking, is that . . .; *that* oblig.; *that*-clause C of S; *or* Our conclusion, that there is only enough . . ., has been reached . . .; *that* oblig.; *that*-clause in non-restrictive apposition to S. *8*. We must face the fact that . . .; *that* usually oblig.; *that*-clause in restricted apposition to O. *9*. I am convinced that we cannot . . . and that the results . . .; *that* oblig. both times; *that*-clauses C of *convinced*. *10*. How can I convince you that we have almost . . .; *that* usually oblig.; *that*-clause Od of *convince*.

Ex. 180 *1*. No one ever discovered what caused . . . , O. *2*. . . . to estimate what damage the explosion caused, O. *3*. Where the fire started was . . . , S. *4*. . . . depends on when the fever began, C of preposition, *on*. *5*. I am not quite sure when the fever began, C of adj. *sure*. *6*. I can never remember which drawer he keeps . . . , O. *7*. My problem is how we can reduce . . . , C of S. *8*. The question why he didn't say . . . is irrelevant . . . , in apposition to S. *9*. I cannot tell you precisely how often these fevers occur, O. *10*. I am concerned about how much all this will cost, C. of prep., *about*.

Ex. 181 *1*. . . . where to put . . . *2*. Where to put . . . *3*. . . . where to put . . . *4*. —— *5*. —— *6*. . . . what to do. *7*. . . . how to open. *8*. . . . when to start. *9*. —— *10*. ——. An infinitive *wh*-clause cannot be formed (a) with *why*, (b) unless the subject of the infinitive clause has the same referent as the subject of a monotransitive verb in the superordinate clause or as the indirect object of a ditransitive verb, and (c) if the tense in the superordinate clause is present and the tense in the infinitive clause is past, and *vice versa*.

Ex. 182 *1*. I wonder if/whether you are . . . *2*. He asked me if/whether I was . . . *3*. I don't care whether you are . . . or not. *4*. Whether it costs too much (or not) depends on how badly . . . *5*. My decision will depend on whether it costs too much. *6*. Whether it is . . . or not is the crucial question. *7*. I'm not interested in whether it can be . . . *8*. I am not sure if/whether it is . . .

Ex. 183 *1*. *Wh*-interrog. *2*. nominal relative. *3*. could be either. *4*. *Wh*-interrog. *5*. nom. rel. *6*. *Wh*-interrog. *7*. nom. rel. *8*. *Wh*-interrog. *9*. could be either. *10*. nom. rel.

Ex. 184 Examples: *1*. a. I'll give you the particular thing you want; b. I'll give you anything you want, no matter what it is.

Ex. 185 *1*. a. Od; b. I in both. *2*. a. Od; b. I, everyone. *3*. a. Od; b. I in both. *4*. a. C of S; b. the plan, we. *5*. a. in apposition to S; b. the plan, we. *6*. a. S; b. the whole dependent clause, anyone. *7*. a. S; b. the whole dependent clause, Osbert.

Ex. 186 *1.* Od. *2.* S. *3.* apposition to S. *4.* C of preposition. *5.* A.
Ex. 187 *1.* surprised at his making . . . *2.* His being an astronaut accounted for . . . *3.* . . . object to your finishing . . . *4.* . . . approve of my having . . . *5.* . . . realize that W's speaking to the press would . . . *6.* His speaking to the press about this has . . . *7.* Do you mind my not coming . . . ? *8.* . . . that meant our not having sufficient time . . .
Ex. 188 *1.* —— *2.* When living in W., . . . *3.* Since meeting you, . . . *4.* Once published, your book . . . *5.* When in Rome, . . . *6.* Until asked to speak, . . . *7.* Before serving in the army, . . . *8.* While in the army, . . . *9.* (On) entering the town, . . . *10.* After travelling (*or* After having travelled) . . .
Ex. 189 *1.* a. *2.* a. *3.* b. *4.* b. *5.* b. *6.* a *or* b. *7.* a. *8.* a. *9.* b *or* a. *10.* a *or* b.
Ex. 190 Examples: *1.* If you stand up here, (then) . . . *2.* Unless you stand up, . . . *or* You won't be able to see . . . if you don't stand up. *3.* You won't see anything unless you stand up here. *4.* Although we strained our eyes, . . . *5.* Even if you strain your eyes, . . . *6.* Even if/though you had the best . . . *7.* I will let you come . . . on condition that you do . . . *8.* If this story were true, it would be . . . *9.* If that had really happened, we would all have been dead . . . *10.* If you should need any help, . . . *11.* If only you had telephoned me, . . . *12.* Whatever I say, . . . *13.* Whether you tell me or not, . . . *14.* Whatever the solution may be, . . . *15.* However great his difficulties were, he always . . .
Ex. 191 *1.* adjunct, a. *2.* disjunct. *3.* disjunct. *4.* adjunct, b. *5.* adjunct, a. *6.* adjunct, a. *7.* adjunct, b. *8.* adjunct, b.
Ex. 192 *1.* —— *2.* Yes, so as/in order/to. *3.* —— *4.* Yes, so as/in order/to. *5.* —— *6.* Yes, so as/in order/to. *7.* Yes, so as/in order/to. *8.* —— *9.* —— *10.* Yes, so as/in order/to.
Ex. 193 *1.* b. *2.* a *or* b. *3.* a. *4.* a. *5.* b.
Ex. 194 *1.* as, as. *2.* as, the way. *3.* as if, as though. *4.* as if, as though. *5.* as if, as though. *6.* as, in the way that, in any way (that). *7.* in the way that.
Ex. 195 *1.* As, so. *2.* the sooner. *3.* As. *4.* Rather than. *5.* rather than *or* instead of.
Ex. 196 *2.* Since I spoke clearly, everyone . . . *or* Speaking clearly, I made myself heard by everyone . . . *4.* When the trees are fully grown, the men . . . *5.* Put the *-ing* clause at the end. *7.* Put the *-ing* clause at the end.
Ex. 197 *1.* Od. *2.* S. *3.* Oi. *4.* A. *5.* Cs.
Ex. 198 *1.* We have greater power . . . than our fathers had. *2.* There were astrologers more intelligent than . . . *3.* We need a greater number of highly trained scientists *or* scientists who are more highly trained.
Ex. 199 *1.* S. *2.* O *or* S. *3.* S. *4.* O. *5.* S. *6.* O. *7.* S. *8.* O. *9.* S. *10.* O *or* S.
Ex. 200 Examples: *1.* He was so eloquent that he convinced . . . *2.* He was so eloquent a speaker that . . . *7.* So eloquent was he that . . .
Ex. 201 *1.* —— *2.* Yes, as main clause. *3.* Yes, as main clause. *4.* —— *5.* Yes, as adverbial. *6.* —— *7.* Yes, as main. *8.* —— *9.* Yes, as *to*-infinitive clause, style disjunct. *10.* Yes, as nominal relative disjunct. *11.* —— *12.* ——

13. —— *14*. Yes, *-ing* clause, disjunct. *15*. Yes, *-ed* clause, disjunct. *16*. ——
17. —— *18*. Yes, main clause. *19*. Yes, main. *20*. Yes, main. *21*. Yes, main.
Ex. 202 When the comment clause comes at the end, nuclear stress precedes it. The comment clause is then spoken on a low, level pitch, except after a *yes–no* question (eg 21), when it is spoken on a high, level pitch. When the comment clause comes elsewhere, it has an intonation pattern separated from that of the rest of the sentence.
Ex. 203 Examples: *1*. If you arrive . . . , please telephone . . . *2*. I will leave a message . . . in case I am out . . . *3*. If I have left my office when you arrive, please . . . *4*. Do not make any appointments before I (have) discuss(ed) your programme . . . *5*. You can start making appointments as soon as we agree . . . *6*. Do not make any appointments unless I approve. *7*. You will be free . . . when, *or* after, you have finished . . . *8*. If you do not carry (*or* have not carried) out . . . , you will have to come back . . . *9*. If you (should) run into difficulties, consult me before you proceed. *10*. I will not interfere unless . . .
Ex. 204 Examples: *1*. Yes, it's time we left now. *2*. Yes, he talks as if he knew all the answers. *3*. No, but he behaves as if he were. *4*. I'd rather we didn't stop now. *5*. No, but let's suppose this were our own house. *6*. Indeed, if only I had enough money . . . *7*. Yes, we could really have fun if George were here. *8*. Yes, I would have been . . . if the police had stopped me. *9*. . . . if it weren't for that old lady's hat. *10*. . . . if you hadn't stepped . . .
Ex. 205 *1*. Since my parents came . . . , they have been . . . *2*. Since they have lived here, they have made . . . *3*. Since J. left A., she has hardly eaten . . . *4*. Since A. has been . . . , she has refused . . . *5*. Ever since I heard that song it has been ringing in my ears. *6*. Since R. was living in Rome, I have not had . . . *7*. Since G. began listening to English recordings, his pronunciation has greatly improved. *8*. Since he has been listening . . . , he has not been spending . . .
Ex. 206 *1*. . . . that the Committee adjourn and meet . . . *2*. . . . that this meeting be adjourned . . . *3*. If this report be true, . . . *4*. If this report were . . . , . . . *5*. Though there be . . . , . . . *6*. . . . as if he alone were . . . *7*. Suppose every word of this were . . . , . . . *8*. If the truth be known . . ., . . . *9*. If the truth were known, . . . *10*. Whatever be the difficulties . . . , . . .
Ex. 207 *1*. *No change*. *2*. . . . that you should have . . . *3*. . . . that we should have to take . . . *4*. . . . quite right that you should speak . . . *5*. *stet*. *6*. . . . surprised that you should say . . . *7*. . . . why you should insist . . . *8*. *stet* *9*. . . . why he should have refused . . . *10*. . . . should be published . . .
Ex. 208 *a*. He told me that he knew the answer and that I needed a P.P. I replied that that would be all right and asked him to find me one. He said that all I had to do was to send a boy down to the city, to a certain address. *b*. He said that he had heard a well-known actor on the radio the day before. The actor was asked to imagine he were left alone on a desert island and were allowed to take just one luxury with him. He was then asked to say what he would choose.

He said he would take a telephone and would push the wire into the sand. His greatest pleasure would then be to sit and look at it and to think that it would never ring and he would never have to answer it.

Ex. 209 Example: The interviewer asked Dr. S. if it was true that he had been living for over a year with gorillas. Dr. S. said that that was quite true. He was then asked how long he had spent with his gorillas in all. He replied that he had been in A. for a term of twenty months. The gorillas had soon become quite used to his presence. Dr. S. went on to explain that when he arrived at the edge of their group, the gorillas looked up . . . routine. The interviewer asked if the gorillas really live(d) in groups. Dr. S. confirmed that; and added that each group consists/consisted of from five to thirty animals.

Ex. 210 Where was he, he wondered. This was N., wasn't it? Or had he left the train at the wrong station? No, he hadn't. There, . . . , he could see the sign: N. Then why was there no one to meet him? Surely they must have had his telegram? How could they leave him to find his own way, with all his luggage, in this . . . Well, he would put his suitcases . . . But where should he walk to? He remembered now. They had written to tell him the house . . . Even then, he couldn't believe they expected him to find his way . . . like this.

Ex. 211 *1.* b. *2.* g. *3.* f. *4.* b *or* f. *5.* b. *6.* d. *7.* e. *8.* a. *9.* c. *10.* b. *11.* e. *12.* g. *13.* a. *14.* f. *15.* d. *16.* a. *17.* f. *18.* h. *19.* e. *20.* h. *21.* e. *22.* b. *23.* d. *24.* f. *25.* d. *26.* a. *27.* f. *28.* b. *29.* c. *30.* h.

Ex. 212 *1.* Back up it. *2.* Back them up. *3.* Call it off. *4.* Come off it. *5.* Get over it. *6.* Get it over. *7.* Swim across it. *8.* Put it across. *9.* run in it. *10.* Run it in. *11.* Step up it. *12.* Step it up. *13.* You take after him. *14.* I took to him at once. *15.* You can take it over. *16.* Don't turn it on. *17.* The dog turned on him. *18.* Turn down it. *19.* Turn it down. *20.* Now wind it up.

Ex. 213 *1.* a, c. *2.* c. *3.* c. sometimes b. *4.* b, d. *5.* a, b. *6.* a. c. *7.* c, sometimes a. *8.* c. *9.* a, c. *10.* b, d.

Ex. 214 *1.* . . . brought their children up strictly. *2. stet. 3.* . . . break the party up. *4. stet. 5. stet. 6.* . . . send off this telegram . . . *7. stet. 8.* . . . take your coat off? *9.* . . . find the answer out somehow. *10.* . . . run that child over.

Ex. 215 *1.* This question will be brought up . . . *2.* It will then be dealt with . . . *3.* Has this matter been looked into? *4.* This argument is not borne out by the facts. *5.* This house has never been looked after . . . *6.* Are you being attended to? *7.* My application has been turned down. *8.* The N.B. was broken into . . . *9.* Any foreigner, however innocent, was set upon. *10.* This job must be got on with.

Ex. 216 Examples: *1.* That is the article we were just talking about. *2.* This is the bed Q.E. slept in. *3.* That is the agreement I want to back out of.

Ex. 217 Nuclear stress falls on the particle when it is final, as in Ex. 215, item 7 and Ex. 216, items 4 & 5. The particle is also stressed in Ex. 215, items 1, 4 & 10 and Ex. 216, items 3, 8, 9 & 10. The preposition, as in Ex. 215, items 2, 6 & 10, is unstressed if monosyllabic.

Ex. 218 *1*. b, c, j. *2*. a, b, c, g, j, k, m. *3*. a, b, c, e, g, h, k, m. *4*. a, b, d, h, k. *5*. a, b, c, f, h, k, l, n, o. *6*. b, k, n. *7*. a, b, c, h, i, j, k, m. *8*. a, b, c, d, e, g, h, k, o. *9*. a, b, c, f, h, k, m; *get mad* also possible in the sense of *get angry*. *10*. a, b, c, e, g, h, j, k. *11*. b. *12*. b. *13*. a, b, d, h, k, m. *14*. b, j. *15*. a, b, k, m.
Ex. 219 *1*. to noise. *2*. (of me). *3*. (with us). *4*. to anyone. *5*. (about Mary). *6*. (of yourself). *7*. to hard work. *8*. of that. *9*. for home. *10*. (with my accounts). *11*. of anything. *12*. of success. *13*. (about this sentence). *14*. (about Mary). *15*. in *or* with this project. *16*. of the danger. *17*. about dancing. *18*. our appeal. *19*. to us. *20*. (on us). *21*. (from cheese). *22*. for promotion. *23*. for more responsibility. *24*. (of anyone). *25*. to the task. *26*. at anything. *27*. (to me). *28*. with this town. *29*. for this job. *30*. of Mary. *31*. (about your prize). *32*. of a rest. *33*. at chemistry. *34*. (for your help). *35*. (to you). *36*. (on me). *37*. for knowledge. *38*. of those facts. *39*. (of others). *40*. to anyone. *41*. on his work. *42*. (of her). *43*. (on swimming). *44*. (to your friends). *45*. to me. *46*. (of you). *47*. (for a meal). *48*. (from danger). *49*. in languages. *50*. of this exercise.
Ex. 220 *1*. The Countess was amused at . . . *2*. He was annoyed at the way . . . *3*. Everybody was atonished at . . . *4*. He was obviously not bothered with . . . *5*. He was not contented with . . . *6*. The Countess, however, was delighted with . . . *7*. I am not disappointed in *or* with you. *8*. Don't get excited by . . . *9*. He was fascinated by . . . *10*. He was already interested in . . . *11*. The Countess was very pleased with . . . *12*. She was completely satisfied with . . . *13*. . . . she had been shocked by . . . *14*. His old father would have been surprised at . . . *15*. Now, his father would not have been worried about . . .
Ex. 221 *1*. We are adamant that you should resign. *2*. We are afraid that you have . . . *3*. I'm ashamed that you should have behaved . . . *4*. I am certain that there will be . . . *5*. We are concerned that you should feel . . . *6*. We are fully confident that you will . . . *7*. It is curious that you should say . . . *8*. We're delighted that you see . . . *9*. It is essential that you should have . . . *10*. The Captain is furious that you (should have) revealed . . . *11*. We feel . . . honoured that you (should) have received us . . . *12*. We are happy that you (should) feel at home . . . *13*. Everyone is insistent that you should prolong . . . *14*. We are greatly relieved that we shall have . . . *15*. I am deeply shocked that you should have been kept waiting . . . *16*. My husband is very sorry that he will not be . . . *17*. I'm not sure yet that I'll be able to come . . . *18*. Is it true (that) you said that? *19*. I'm surprised (that) you don't know . . . *20*. It is vital that everyone (should) vote . . .
Ex. 222 *1*. d. *2*. c. *3*. a. *4*. b. *5*. e. *6*. d. *7*. e. *8*. e. *9*. d. *10*. a. *11*. b. *12*. d. *13*. c. *14*. a. *15*. c.
Ex. 223 *1*. I very much want to . . . *2*. We received your telegram and were delighted. *3*. It was sensible of you to . . . *4*. The clerk answered the call promptly. *5*. It is easy to remember this rule. *6*. We do not want to leave . . . *7*. It is not difficult to heat our house. *8*. It is difficult to find it. *9*. Can you leave? *10*. It would be foolish of you to . . . *11*. J. sees the point quickly. *12*. He very

much wants to . . . *13.* We have him as a friend and are proud of it. *14.* It was rude of me not to . . . *15.* We have you with us . . . and are happy.

Ex. 224 *ask*, a (a question), c (that something should be done), d (what was done), e (to leave). *believe*, a (your story), c (that you told the truth), d (what you told me). *consider*, a (your application), c (that you were right), d (what we should do), f (leaving early). *deny*, a, c, f. *enjoy*, a, f. *explain*, a, c, d. *feel*, a, c. *gather*, a, c, d. *hope*, c, e *keep*, a, b (eg keep you away from your work), f (eg keep talking). *lay*, a, b. *mind*, a, d, f. *need*, a, e, f. *owe*, a. *place*, a, b. *remember*, a, c, d, e, f. *approve of*, a, d, f. *depend on*, a, d, f. *make up*, a. *point out*, a, c, d.

Ex. 225 *1.* This house was built in 1968. *2.* The G.P. was built by K.K. *3.* —— *4.* —— *5.* Have they been weighed recently? *6.* New opinions are usually opposed. *7.* My attention was held by a man with a scar across his face. *8.* —— *9.* He had been admitted by accident. *10.* His hair must have been dyed. *11.* —— *12.* —— *13.* —— *14.* —— *15.* Your record has never been equalled. *16.* I would like to be measured for a suit. *17.* —— *18.* —— *19.* The principle known as Boyle's Law was discovered by R.B. *20.* This property has already been sold.

Ex. 226 *1.* I admit (that) I have . . . *2.* I wonder if/whether I have . . . *3.* I doubt if/whether I have . . . *4.* I don't doubt that you have . . . *5.* I agree (that) you wrote . . . *6.* I agree (that) you should pay . . . *7.* We agreed (that) you were going . . . *8.* We decided (that) we had . . . *9.* We could not decide if/whether we should continue . . . *10.* We had to decide quickly how we could . . . *11.* We have all decided (that) you should go . . . *12.* I expect (that) help will arrive . . . *13.* May I ask what you intend . . . ? *14.* May I ask if/whether we are to stay . . . *15.* All I ask is that you (should) tell us . . . *16.* I suggest (that) we (should) divide . . . *17.* I remember this is where . . . *18.* Do you remember if/whether we took . . . ? *19.* Ah, now I know where we went wrong. *20.* I sincerely regret that you (should) no longer trust . . .

Ex. 227 *a.* non-finite, inf. clause, without subj., obj. of *wanted*; *b.* non-finite *-ing* cl., without subj., obj. of *enjoyed*; *c.* non-finite inf. clause, subj. *you*, obj. of *expected*; *d.* non-finite, bare inf. cl., subj. *they*, obj. of *heard*; *e.* non-finite, *-ing* clause, subj. *they*, obj. of *saw*; *f.* non-finite *-ed* cl., subj. *my seat*, obj. of *found*.

Ex. 228 *1.* a, c. *2.* b. *3.* a, b. *4.* a, c. *5.* e, f. *6.* b. *7.* a, d, e, f. *8.* a, c, d. *9.* a. *10.* b, c, e, f. *11.* b, e, f. *12.* a, b, c, e, f. *13.* a, c. *14.* a. *15.* b, e. *16.* b. *17.* c. *18.* a. *19.* d, e, f. *20.* a, c.

Ex. 229 Examples: *1.* a. I remembered that I had to fill up the form, so I filled it up; b. I filled up the form, and remember having done so. *2.* a. I did not wake you this morning. I forgot to.; b. I forgot I had to wake you. *3.* a. I have to tell you this story, and I am sorry I must do so.; b. I told you that story and regret having done so. *4.* a. I made an attempt to turn the key . . .; b. I experimented by turning the key . . . *5.* a. I learnt to ride. My father taught me.; b. He gave me lessons in riding. *6.* a. He made us all empty . . .; b. We were all emptying our pockets because of something he said or did. *7.* a. You deserve to be the first

who will shoot.; b. You ought to be shot before that can happen. *8.* That boy wants to see what is happening.; b. That boy ought to be watched.
Ex. 230 *1.* mono; That a mistake had been made was admitted *or* It was admitted that . . . *2.* complex; The mistake was considered (to be) very serious. *3.* complex; You are considered (to be) one of our . . . *4.* mono; That you . . . was fully recognized *or* It was recognized that . . . *5.* complex; You are found (to be) innocent . . . *6.* complex; Your companion is known to be a trouble-maker. *7.* complex; Your story has been proved (to be) . . . *8.* complex; However, you are thought (to be), at times, . . . *9.* complex; You are expected to show . . . *10.* mono; That . . . is regretted *or* It is regretted that . . . *11.* complex; Two planes have been reported (to be) missing. *12.* complex; You were meant to complete . . .; and return . . .
Ex. 231 *1.* —— *2.* . . . of your . . . *3.* . . . my opening . . . *4.* —— *5.* —— *6.* . . . John's telling . . . *7.* —— *8.* —— *9.* —— *10.* . . . their being given . . .
Ex. 232 *1.* I want you (or someone else) to do . . . *2.* I want to see that you (or someone else) have done it . . . *3.* We found that someone had done the work . . . *4.* I have heard people repeat . . . *5.* Can you ask someone to copy . . . *6.* . . . we must ask someone to cut . . . *7.* . . . George has had an accident and now his leg is broken. *8.* I would like you, or the cook, to fry my egg. *9.* It was reported that £6000 had been stolen. *10.* Didn't you hear someone call . . . ?
Ex. 233 *1.* b, c, d, e, g, k. *2.* a, b, d, e, f, g, o, p, q, r. *3.* a, d, f, o, p, r. *4.* c, d, e, h, k. *5.* d, h, k. *6.* d, e, j, o, q. *7.* h, i, m. *8.* l, q. *9.* h, i, k, m, n. *10.* c, d, e.
Ex. 234 *1.* b, c, d, e, g, k. *2.* b, g. *3.* a, f, o, p, r. *4.* d, j, l, q. *5.* d, e.
Ex. 235 *1.* a. —; b. . . . made her very angry. *2.* a. . . . broken her wardrobe open; b, . . . broken it open. *3.* a. . . . set all the prisoners free; b. . . . . . . set them all free. *4.* a. . . . make possible the end of . . . ?; b. . . . make it possible? *5.* a. . . . have the minutes of our last two meetings ready for . . . ?; b. . . . have them ready for . . . ? *6.* a. . . . leave those two . . . by the window clear; b. . . . leave them clear. *7.* a. preferably not mobile; b. . . . appoint them officers of the society.
Ex. 236 *1.* —— *2.* I have asked a great favour of you. *3.* . . . booked a double room . . . for you. *4.* Bring your essay to me . . . *5.* . . . brought some grapes for us. *6.* Call a taxi for me . . . *7.* . . . cash a cheque for me? *8.* . . . caused so much trouble for you. *9.* —— *10.* . . . done much good to me. *11.* . . . give all . . . to you. *12.* . . . handed this message to me. *13.* . . . leave your dinner for you . . . *or* your dinner . . . for you. *14.* . . . left a small fortune to *or* for her. *15.* . . . owe anything to . . . ? *16.* . . . paid the whole sum to G. *17.* . . . show your ticket to me. *18.* . . . told the truth to you. *19.* Throw that towel to me . . . ? *20.* I wish good luck to you.
Ex. 237 *a.* Oi can be omitted in all the 20 sentences except 1, 11, 12, 19 & 20. *b.* Od can be ellipted in 2, 16, 17 & 18.
Ex. 238 *2.* You have been asked a great . . . A great favour has been asked of you. *3.* You were booked a . . . A double room was booked. *8.* You have been

caused . . . So much trouble has been caused (you). *11.* You will be given . . . All the necessary information will be given (you). *12.* I have just been handed . . . This message has just been handed me. *14.* She was left a . . . A small fortune was left her. *16.* G. has been paid the . . . The whole sum has been paid. *17.* I must be shown your ticket. Your ticket must be shown. *18.* You have been told . . . The truth has been told (you).

Ex. 239 *a.* 1. of; 2. for; 3. to; 4. for; 5. on; 6. with; 7. to *or* with; 8. to; 9. on; 10. on *or* about; 11. with; 12. of; 13. to; 14. from; 15. from; 16. of; 17. in; 18. to; 19. for; 20. with; 21. to; 22. with; 23. for. *b.* The prep. phrase could be ellipted except in 3, 5, 7, 8, 12, 13, 20, 22. *c.* Examples: 1. B. was accused of . . . 2. A. was admired for . . . 3. You have been assigned to . . . *d.* Examples: 1. What crime was B. accused of? 2. What qualities was A. admired for? 3. What task have you been assigned to?

Ex. 240 *a.* 1. lose; 2. making; 3. put; 4. set; 5. kept. *b.* 1. Your main objective must not be lost sight of. 2. I don't like being made fun of. 3. It is time this nonsense was put a stop to. 4. Three haystacks were set fire to. 5. The latest research has not been kept pace with.

Ex. 241 *a.* 1. taken; 2. take; 3. made; 4. taken *or* made; 5. taken. *b.* Examples: 1. This equipment has not been taken proper care of. Proper care has not been taken of this equipment. 2. I hope my absence will not be taken advantage of. I hope advantage will not be taken of my absence. 5. These instructions have not been taken notice of. No notice has been taken . . .

Ex. 242 1. a, c. *2.* a, c. *3.* b. *4.* a, c. *5.* b. *6.* a, c. *7.* a, c. *8.* b. *9.* a, c. *10.* b. *11.* a, c. *12.* a, b. *13.* a, c. *14.* b. *15.* a, c. *16.* a, c. *17.* a, c. *18.* a, c. *19.* b. *20.* a, b.

Ex. 243 *1.* I persuaded J. to see . . . *2.* —— *3.* —— *4.* I advised him to stay . . . *5.* I warned him not to go out. *6.* —— *7.* I reminded him to take . . . *8.* —— *9.* I requested him to keep . . . *10.* ——

Ex. 244 *1.* A. *2.* A. *3.* B. *4.* B. *5.* A. *6.* B. *7.* A. *8.* B. *9.* B. *10.* B.

Ex. 245 *1.* poor, b; old, b. *2.* devoted, b; elder, a. *3.* beautiful, b; in the hall, a. *4.* sports, a; light, a *or* b; cotton, a; open-toed, a. *5.* who went to school with me, a. *6.* great, b; of 1666, a; of a baker, a. *7.* sensible, b; good, b; old, b. *8.* old, a; ill, a. *9.* thriving, a; Inca, a; of the Spaniard, a. *10.* long-haired, a; strangely dressed, a; stately, b. *11.* who called here last night, a. *12.* who called here last night, b. *13.* to which we were taken, a; oldest, a. *14.* to which we were taken every week, b; great, a. *15.* which have been given to us by well-wishers, b. *16.* you see here, a. *17.* whose names are below the line on this list, a. *18.* whose names . . . police, b. *19.* which is . . . June, b. *20.* which I never planted in it, a.

Ex. 246 Examples: *1.* a. . . . wearing the overcoat; . . . carrying the overcoat; b. . . . who is wearing . . . ; . . . who was wearing . . . *2.* a. . . . working in the garden; . . . sitting in the garden. *b.* . . . who is working . . . ; . . . who was working . . .

Ex. 247 Examples: *1.* By putting the adverbial adjunct, *with my staff,* after the noun phrase modifier, *of stocking the new pig farm,* the writer gives the impression that the farm will be stocked with his staff. This could be avoided if the adv. adj. were placed immediately after *discussed. 5*. Say 'A copy of this book on breast-feeding can be bought at your local bookstore'. *6*. Someone 'on the make' is someone trying to make a quick profit. Misunderstanding could be avoided by wording the dependent finite clause thus: you should seek advice on the make from an expert.

Ex. 248 *1*. which, 0. *2*. which. *3*. who. *4*. 0. *5*. which. *6*. who. *7*. which. *8*. who. *9*. which. *10*. who.

Ex. 249 *1*. . . . which I was speaking about, . . . that I was speaking about, . . . the article I was speaking about. *2*. which *or* that will tell you . . . *3*. which/that/0 that quotation was taken from? *4*. . . . whom/who/that/0 you were referring to? *5*. . . . whom/who/that/0 I have the greatest respect for. *6*. . . . which/that/0 Shakespeare was born in? *7*. . . . the very day that/when I first saw M. *8*. . . . the way that/0 you received us. *9*. and *10*. No variation possible.

Ex. 250 *1*. the theatre. *2*. *either* the theatre *or* the whole previous clause. *3*. the whole previous clause. *4*. *either* five encores *or* the whole previous clause. *5*. five encores. *6*. the whole previous clause. *7*. the mountainside. *8*. the whole previous clause. *9*. the whole previous clause. *10*. every bottle of Buzz.

Ex. 251 *1*. The belief that the earth is flat is still held . . . , (a) *2*. The truth, that the earth is round, has been evident . . . , (b) *3*. Columbus's assumption that . . . was soon proved wrong, (a) *4*. C's report that . . . lured many explorers . . . (a) *5*. The suspicion that . . . rests on . . . (a) *6*. When scientists advanced the argument that . . . , this was not well received . . . (a) *7*. The fact that you went to sleep . . . does not exempt you . . . (a) *8*. This fact, that you went to sleep . . . , suggests . . . (b) *9*. I cannot accept your excuse that people . . . , (a) *10*. The knowledge that . . . is a great comfort . . . , (a).

Ex. 252 *1*. who was carrying *or* carried. *2*. who weighed. *3*. which came *or* was coming *or* had come. *4*. which was (being) driven. *5*. who does not have. *6*. which is standing. *7*. which was *or* had been left. *8*. which are not *or* have not been declared. *9*. which cost. *10*. who did not hear. *11*. who heard *or* had heard. *12*. which was, *or* had been, burnt down.

Ex. 253 *1*. which arrives *or* will arrive. *2*. who flew. *3*. ever to see = who ever saw. *4*. who(m) you should see. *5*. (whom) J. should speak to. *6*. (that) you can eat at. *7*. that you should get there. *8*. The way you can get . . . *9*. that I can read. *10*. that you can do. *11*. that we should consider. *12*. that must be considered.

Ex. 254 *1*. Our plan to cross the river . . . failed. *2*. Our appeal to volunteer for another attempt . . . *3*. . . . the idea to create a diversion . . . *4*. We had no wish to waste lives . . . *5*. Our allies' promise to send reinforcements was not fulfilled. *6*. We felt their hesitation to come . . . was cowardly. *7*. Their refusal to fulfil their promise . . . *8*. This increased our determination to succeed . . . *9*. . . . we were not disturbed by the enemy's threat to attack us. *10*. . . . deceived by their proposal to call . . .

Ex. 255 Examples: *1*. . . . that stands by the church. *2*. . . . which was painted by . . . *3*. . . . which is bound for M. *4*. . . . which will be suitable for M. *5*. . . . which is suitable for all . . . *6*. . . . who is qualified for . . . *7*. . . . who is (talking) with your wife . . . *8*. . . . who has a gun. *9*. . . . who has no hat. *10*. . . . who comes from P. *11*. . . . which is taken from S. *12*. . . . which should be followed if there is . . . *13*. . . . which is, *or* will be, given by your company. *14*. . . . who has a strong will. *15*. . . . who owns property. *16*. . . . who is one of my acquaintance. *17*. . . . which is part of our cellar. *18*. . . . who live in Asia. *18*. . . . which is exercised by the majority. *19*. A man who tries to practise every trade.

Ex. 256 Examples: *1*. the officer responsible for navigating. *2*. a fascination from which I could not escape. *3*. a dexterity which came without thinking. *4*. the servants who were paid, a definite position.

Ex. 257 *1*. Yes, v: This is very alarming news. *2*. Yes, v: G. is a very amusing man. *3*. No. *4*. Yes, v. *5*. No. *6*. Yes: Those (They) are very well behaved children. *7*. No. *8*. Yes, v: There are many very bored faces . . . *9*. Yes, ——: That is a burning candle. *10*. No. *11*. Yes, v: This is a very encouraging report. *12*. Yes, ——: This is a lasting agreement. *13*. Yes, v: . . . a very limited supply . . . *14*. Yes, ——: Those are reserved seats. *15*. Yes, v: Those were very satisfied clients. *16*. ——. *17*. Yes, v: This is a very unexpected result. *18*. Yes, v: These are very worrying circumstances.

Ex. 258 Examples: *1*. a. They got married then; b. They were already married then. *2*. a. She has that (permanent) characteristic; b. He is performing that action. *3*. a. It has that characteristic; b. He is performing that action. *4*. a. *painting that picture* = noun postmodifier; b. *is painting* = finite verb. *5*. a. You are performing that action; b. They have that characteristic. *6*. a. He is saying too much to you; b. He has that characteristic.

Ex. 259 *1*. (a) well-built (house). *2*. above-mentioned (article). *3*. badly-needed. *4*. closely-kept. *5*. untold. *6*. unheard of (cruelty). *7*. oil-fired. *8*. blue-eyed. *9*. red-nosed. *10*. heavy-handed. *11*. sabre-toothed. *12*. flat-bottomed.

Ex. 260 *1*. supply of water. *2*. service of motor-buses. *3*. personnel engaged in doing repairs. *4*. sciences about life. *5*. production of protein derived from fish. *6*. a probe into space. *7*. a signal sent by radio. *8*. a plant to produce power. *9*. (electric) power required at the peak (= busiest) hours. *10*. rate of the rise in prices. *11*. blocks composed of graphite. *12*. possibilities of obtaining water from the ground. *13*. hydrology related to the (earth's) surface. *14*. capacity for storing. *15*. the foundation of the dam. *16*. a canal to divert water. *17*. component parts of gear required for landing. *18*. strength (of metal) capable of withstanding shock on impact. *19*. change in volume. *20*. legislation for the prevention of accidents.

Ex. 261 *1*. a short man with red hair. *2*. a fox terrier (= kind of dog) with short hair. *3*. small office containing very little furniture. *4*. a very modest man who is totally committed to some ideal. *5*. quite considerable expenses for entertainment. *6*. two attractive villas with flat roofs. *7*. attractive apartments, each with two bedrooms. *8.* elegant houses characteristic of a certain period and of urban architecture. *9.* someone who advises boys and girls, who are still at school, on the careers they could later follow. *10.* new jackets made of leather and on sale at reasonable prices.

Ex. 262 *1.* two beautifully-carved oak chairs. *2.* Your old blue Japanese silk scarf. *3.* This small round iron cooking-pot. *4.* the riverside villa murder. *5.* their neat white smog masks. *6.* several thousand recently-stolen unused insurance stamps. *7.* all these broken, shrivelled walnut shells. *8.* a famous Scottish medical school. *9.* the country's best-selling cultivator. *10.* a very picturesque, slightly crumbling thatch-roofed country cottage.

Ex. 263 Nuclear stress on: *1.* OXford. *2.* uniVERsity. *3.* IN. *4.* FORty. *5.* LEISurely. *6.* MUCH. *7.* DONS. *8.* UN-. *9.* whole-HEARTedly. *10.* UP.

Ex. 264 Nuclear stress on: *1.* AM. *2.* HAVE. *3.* DO, DO. *4.* DID. *5.* MIGHT. *6.* MUST. *7.* MUST. *8.* CAN'T. *9.* ARE, THAT's, ARE. *10.* WILL.

Ex. 265 *1.* It was invented by G.B. *2.* No, America was discovered in the . . . by N. *3.* Influenza is caused by two . . . *4.* Because the ingredients are first cut up very small. *5.* It is emitted by the sun. *6.* Their board and lodging was (*or* were) provided by the master.

Ex. 266 *1.* a & b. my husband, S. *2.* a. he; b. that heavy trunk, Od. *3.* a. a young man; b. not one girl in ten, Od. *4.* a. I; b. a scandal, Co. *5.* a. you; b. an angel, Cs. *6.* a. he; b. that shelf, C prep. *7.* a. Joe, he; b. fool, Cs; thief, Cs. *8.* a. I; b. break his bloody neck, P. *9.* a. I; b. die, V. *10.* a. there; b. suddenly, conjunct.

Ex. 267 *1.* Down fell the rain. *2.* Up and up went the prices. *3.* So anxious was he to . . . *4.* Under no circumstances would he give up writing . . . *5.* Just as firm was his determination . . . *6.* Never has it been more difficult . . . *7.* At the far end of the room stood a tall . . ., staring at us. *8.* Only then did we realize . . . *9.* Now mounting the steps is H. M. the E. *10.* In no other country . . . would you witness . . .

Ex. 268 *1.* It was S. who saw . . . It was an enormous serpent that S. saw approaching. *2.* It was Capt. M. who . . . It was this incident that C.M. reported . . . It was to A.G. that C.M. reported . . . *3.* It was to A.G. that he sent a report . . . *4.* It was at Bristol that . . . It was on a dark and cloudy afternoon in 1896 that . . . *5.* It was J.C.'s first novel that was called A.S. It was his first novel that . . . It was A.S. that J.C.'s first novel was called. *6.* It was because . . . questions that the book took . . . to write. *7.* It was after . . . publication that S.M. gave up . . . *8.* It was only after . . . research that . . . *9.* It is the restriction on ether-space that is the dominant constraint . . . *10.* It is its high . . . changes that is the most striking feature . . .

Ex. 269 *1.* . . . that S. saw approaching. *2.* . . . that C.M. reported this incident. *3.* . . . that C.M. reported this incident to. *4.* . . . that the D. docked at. *5.* . . . that was called A.S. *6.* . . . an enormous serpent. *7.* . . . report this incident to A.G. *8.* . . . his first novel had been accepted for publication was S.M.

9. . . . who gave up medicine after . . . *10*. . . . the most striking feature of malaria is . . . *or*. . . malaria is highly endemic with hardly any . . .

Ex. 270 Examples: *1*. It is very easy to answer . . . *2*. It is difficult to understand F. *3*. It is impossible to do business with him. *4*. It is quite likely that he will let . . . *5*. It is known that he double-crosses . . . *6*. It seems that you have taken . . . *7*. Yes, it happens that I have had . . . *8*. It is said that he has been . . . *9*. It appears that you know . . . *10*. It is certain that he will be charged . . .

Ex. 271 *1*. There was a . . . monkey wearing . . . *2*. There were monkeys under the table . . . *3*. There was a boy named G. S. sitting . . . *4*. There were several trains coming . . . *5*. There were things called firesquirts that were used . . . *6*. There were many citizens who believed . . . *7*. There was a bolt on my front door but . . . *8*. There are several thousand . . . in the M. *9*. There were people who believed that . . . *or* There was a belief that . . . *10*. There was an old . . .

Ex. 272 *1*. There should be a stronger light . . . *2*. There must have been a mistake. *3*. We do not want there to be any disturbance. *4*. There being a bus stop . . . is a great advantage. *5*. There being no further business, . . . *6*. On the top . . . there stood an . . . *7*. There will come a time when you will . . . *8*. Is there anyone waiting . . . *9*. There won't be any difficulty, will there? *10*. There haven't been any messages . . ., have there?

Ex. 273 *1*. I think I have some dust . . . *2*. You have mud . . . *3*. My father has a friend in the M. *4*. I have two questions that I wish to raise. . . . *5*. I have something important . . .

Ex. 274 *1*. It is a great pleasure to be with you . . . *2*. It was so kind of you to . . . *3*. It would be a pity to . . . *4*. It does not matter . . . what you say. *5*. It is a mystery how he came . . . *6*. I think it would be a good idea to . . . *7*. It is regretted that you should . . . *8*. It makes me feel sad seeing you . . . *9*. It was rather complicated getting . . . *10*. Do you find it very dull living here? *11*. I find it impossible to . . . *12*. We must leave it to you to decide what must be done.

Ex. 275 *1*. That loaf was stale that you sold me. *2*. The time has now come to face . . . *3*. A public inquiry was instituted immediately to investigate . . . *4*. The belief is commonly held that . . . *5*. A list will be sent to you of all . . . *6*. A great deal of nonsense is published in the press about . . . *7*. Stories are sometimes told of how . . . *8*. A report has just been issued on meals . . . *9*. The question will arise of how . . . *10*. New evidence has recently been published in support . . .

Ex. 278 See Appendix I of the *Grammar*, I.23–I.32.

Ex. 280 ,, ,, ,, ,, ,, ,, I.33–1.42.

Ex. 281 Consult a good dictionary.

Ex. 282

1. Thinking about it led us to an interesting conCLÙsion.

2. The process of changing a com puter PROgram can be com pared with human DRÈAMS.
3. These bookshelves are be coming very popular in SWÈden. We have recently added an extra UNit to them.
4. Can you tell me when we shall see the reSULTS?
5. May I call you a TÁXi or something?
6. You aren't looking in the right diRÈCtion, I think.
7. I never i magined that such a thing could HÀPpen. Did YÓU?
8. They'll be issuing some new tickets toMÒRrow.
9. Ferguson saw the FÍRE, and Parkinson saw it TOÒ.
10. Are you certain that this is the right RÓAD?
11. How many people were killed in STRÈET accidents last year?
12. None of us have finished Chapter TWÒ yet.
13. Some of the others have finished it alRÈAdy.
14. I have a problem that is much more complicated than THÀT. (*or* much more CÒMplicated than that)
15. What I would like to DÓ is to go somewhere really QUÌet.
16. I am not a ware that I gave you per mission to LÉAVE.
17. That is all I have to TÉLL you, Mrs. F.
18. What he was doing with that gun I can't iMÀGine.
19. What was he doing with that GUN, I wonder.
20. Are there any MÉSsages for me, I wonder?

Ex. 283

1. The monkeys were under the table, perching on chairs, swinging on light fittings.
2. 'I know the answer,' he said. 'You need a Pied Piper.'
3. Leaving us at the gate, they disappeared into the house.
4. Leaving us at the gate like that was rather discourteous.
5. 'Stanley, it's been a long time since we met, hasn't it?'
6. R.B., Scotland's national poet, was born in 1759.
7. The poet R.B. was born at Alloway, Ayrshire.
8. The theatre to which we were taken was the oldest one in P.

9. The theatre, to which we went every week, was a great delight to us.
10. A lawyer by training, when forced by events to be a soldier he proved himself a great soldier.
11. Whatever he had to do he did well, naturally.
12. Whatever he had to do with it, he was not the ringleader.
13. Thirteen thousand houses, nearly one hundred churches, St. Paul's Cathedral, the Royal Exchange, even Guildhall itself went up in flames.
14. In the end(,) they had to resort to gunpowder, blowing up whole rows of houses, and that stopped the fire; that, and the fact that the wind died down.
15. For most of my life, childhood, boyhood and more, we lived in the country.
16. The lawn, almost the only uncontaminated place in that ancient neighbourhood, had hitherto been innocent of any dark secret.
17. The Manager of the Court Theatre put on a play that failed; the (*or* . The) next play he had arranged to put on was not ready(,) and he was at his wits' end. He read a play of mine called L.F., and, though he did not much like it, he thought it might just run for the six weeks till the play he had in mind to follow it with could be produced.
18. Presently the German tutor was aroused, the cordial and intelligent H.S., who explained I had not been expected so soon. He showed me my room, also my bed, but I could not occupy the latter because the out-going English tutor, Bristow, had not yet vacated it.
19. He wants independence; he wants colour in his life. He dreams of achievements none of which seems possible in the village. His reading – and he is an avid reader – seems hardly relevant to his actual life.
20. An image in some way resembles the thing it stands for, whereas a symbol is not like it but represents it arbitrarily. Works of art are images; and a work of art is an image of feeling. Of course a work of art is not an image of feeling only, because we normally do not experience feelings by themselves: we feel towards or about things or people or ideas, so that a work of art, if it is to transmit feelings, must also represent the object towards which the feelings are directed.